Mathematics:
Analysis and Approaches SL
FOR THE IB DIPLOMA

Ian Lucas

PEAK

Published by:
Peak Study Resources Ltd
1 & 3 Kings Meadow
Oxford OX2 0DP
UK

www.peakib.com

Mathematics: Analysis and Approaches SL
Study & Revision Guide for the IB Diploma

ISBN 978-1-913433-02-4

© Ian Lucas 2020

Ian Lucas has asserted his right under the Copyright, Design and Patents Act 1988 to be identified as the author of this work.

Peak Study & Revision Guides for the IB Diploma have been developed independently of the International Baccalaureate Organization (IBO). 'International Baccalaureate' and 'IB' are registered trademarks of the IBO.

Books may be ordered directly through the publisher's website www.peakib.com. For enquiries regarding titles, availability or local stockists, please email books@peakib.com or use the form at www.peakib.com/contact.

Printed and bound in the UK by:
CPI Group (UK) Ltd, Croydon CR0 4YY
www.cpibooks.co.uk

Contents

all

About this book

This is a study guide, not a text book. Its aim is to review each part of the subject and ultimately prepare you for your exams. Covering the complete syllabus, I show you how the topics can translate into questions, giving you plenty of tips and shortcuts.

The exam is not so much a direct test of your knowledge and understanding (you will not get a question which begins "What do you know about...?"); but a test of how you use your knowledge and understanding to solve mathematical problems. So the emphasis in this book is on how to answer questions. In particular you will find plenty of fully worked examples in the text (those similar to Section A exam questions are shaded green), as well as further exercises where it is useful to see how questions can probe a topic from different angles. At the end of each chapter you will find longer questions which are similar in style to those in Section B in the exam – by their nature, such questions may need knowledge of several different areas of the syllabus – and these are indicated with a red band. Answers are provided in the book, but for full working you will need to visit the linked resources page for this guide on the Peak Study Resources website at www.peakib.com/book/3024.

Question (Section A style)	
Worked answer	*Hints and tips*

Question (Section B style)
————
Answer

You are expected to be able to understand and use your graphic display calculator (GDC) to the full in many areas of the syllabus. Indeed, some questions require you to use, for example, the graphing or equation solving features. Since different people use different calculators, it is not possible for this book to explain the detail of their use; but I have indicated calculator tips (using the symbol 🖩), and also questions which require calculator use. The more you can use your GDC, the more proficient you will become.

This book is just one resource that will help you prepare for your exams; another is the set of short videos on the website which lead you through the working and solutions of a wide range of exam-style questions. This area of the website is updated as we add more videos to the resource bank. I have indicated in the text if a question has a video solution: look for the video symbol ▣.

I have liberally splashed notes boxes in the margins throughout the book. These contain hints, warnings, exam tips, "dos and don'ts", suggestions... do read them all, as well as the blue text in the question boxes. There's so much information which can help you with those precious extra marks. And there are similar yellow boxes which contain links to other pages, websites, videos, blogs.

Notes box – please read what they contain!

Reference box; leads you to useful resources.

Acknowledgements

I am enormously grateful to Peter Gray, an IB examiner currently at Munich International School, who has proof read this book and, in the process, made some eminently sensible suggestions for numerous improvements; he has also tactfully pointed to a number of errors in both the text and the calculations which I have gratefully corrected! Any remaining errors are entirely my responsibility, and I would be very happy to hear from readers who find any further errors, or who have suggestions for improvements.

Through my work with Oxford Study Courses I have been privileged, over the last 20 years, to help many students revise towards their IB Mathematics exams, and much of what I have learnt from teaching them has been distilled into this book. I would value any feedback so that later editions can continue to help students around the world. Please feel free to e-mail feedback@peakib.com, or comment via the normal social media channels.

Ian Lucas

The Non-Calculator Paper

The format of the two exam papers is the same – Section A consisting of short answer questions, and Section B comprising extended response questions. However, calculators are only allowed to be used in Paper 2.

It is not intended that Paper 1 will test your ability to perform complicated calculations with the potential for careless errors. It is more to see if you can analyse problems and provide reasoned solutions without using your calculator as a prop. However, this doesn't mean there will be no arithmetic calculations. You should, for example, be able to:

Add and subtract using decimals and fractions

Examples:

$$18.43+12.37; \quad 2\tfrac{1}{2}+3\tfrac{2}{5}$$

Multiply using decimals and fractions

And it would be a good idea to brush up on your multiplication tables – you need them all over the place.

Examples:

$$432 \times 12 \; ; \; 12.6 \times 5 \; ; \; \tfrac{1}{2} \times \tfrac{2}{5} + \tfrac{2}{3} \times \tfrac{1}{4} \; ; \; (2 \times 10^6) \times (5.1 \times 10^{-4})$$

Carry out simple divisions using decimals and fractions

Don't forget that divisions can be written as fractions. For example:

$$9 \div 15 = \tfrac{9}{15} = \tfrac{3}{5} = 0.6$$

Examples:

$$14 \div 0.02 \; ; \; 1\tfrac{1}{2} \div \tfrac{3}{5}$$

Find x as a fraction in its simplest form if $999x = 324$

Fraction simplification can also help with more complex divisions:

eg: Convert 81 km/h to m/s

$$\frac{81 \times 1000}{3600} = \frac{81 \times 10}{36} = \frac{9 \times 10}{4} = \frac{9 \times 5}{2} = \frac{45}{2} = 22.5 \, \text{m/s}$$

Percentage calculations

Examples:

15% of 600kg; Increase 2500 by 12%

What is 150 as a percentage of 500

Quadratic equations

You will be called on to solve quadratic equations many times in the papers. Solving by factorisation is easier than using the formula when you are not using a calculator.

Examples:

Solve $x^2 + 7x - 60 = 0$; $3x^2 - 19x + 20 = 0$

Answers in exact form:

When a question asks for the answer to be in "an exact form" this means it must not be given as a rounded decimal. Typically, the answer will contain one (or more) of the following: square roots, logs, π, e.

Chapter 1: NUMBER AND ALGEBRA

1.1 Number Systems

Different situations require different types of number. For example, populations of countries will always be given as positive whole numbers, whereas the division of a reward will require the use of fractions. These are known as *number systems*, and the ones you need to know are:

- *Natural numbers* – positive whole numbers.
- *Integers* – whole numbers including negatives and zero.
- *Rationals* – numbers which can be written as fractions.
- *Irrationals* – numbers which can't be written as fractions.
- *Reals* – the rationals and the irrationals put together. The reals will include every possible number you could meet in the course.

> You also need to know the conventional symbols used for the main number systems:
> $\mathbb{N}$ = Natural numbers
> $\mathbb{Z}$ = Integers
> $\mathbb{Q}$ = Rational numbers
> $\mathbb{R}$ = Real numbers
> $\mathbb{Z}^+$ = Positive integers

The diagram below shows how the sets are related to each other. For example, every integer can be written as a rational (such as $4 = \frac{4}{1}$), so integers are a subset of rationals.

Reals = Rationals $\cup$ Irrationals

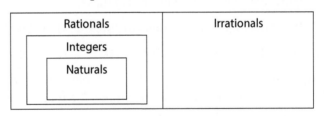

Decimals do not seem to feature in the list above – are they rational or irrational?

- *Recurring decimals* can always be written as fractions so they are rational numbers.
- *Terminating decimals* can also be written as fractions, so they are rational numbers too.
- *Non-recurring, non-terminating decimals* (ie they carry on for ever and never repeat) can never be written as an exact fraction, so they are irrational numbers.

Exact values: $\sqrt{4} = 2$ since 4 is a square number. However, $\sqrt{10}$ cannot be written exactly, like the majority of square roots. It is 3.16228... (the dots indicating that the decimal places continue without recurring). To 4 significant figures $\sqrt{10} = 3.162$, but what do you do if the questions asks you to give an *exact* value? The answer is to use square root notation:

$$x^2 = 10 \Rightarrow x = \sqrt{10}$$

and this (or other equivalent surds) is the only exact way to write down the solution. And, especially if this is an intermediate answer to a question, it is usually better for calculation purposes.

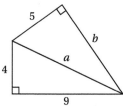

Example: Find the lengths of a and b in the diagram, giving your answers in an exact form.

Solution: $a^2 = 9^2 + 4^2 = 97 \implies a = \sqrt{97}$

               $b^2 = a^2 - 5^2 = 97 - 25 = 72$

               So $b = \sqrt{72}$

The calculation would have been longer (and possibly less accurate) if we had worked out $\sqrt{97}$ as a decimal and used that.

1.2 Accuracy and Standard Form

When answering questions which have numerical solutions, it is important to understand how to round to an appropriate level of accuracy. And for very large or very small numbers, it is necessary to use standard form.

Accuracy: If there are 6 people in a room, then 6 is perfectly accurate. However, a length given as 6 cm implies that it lies between 5.5 cm and 6.5 cm, and these values are known as the *lower* and *upper bounds*. In theory the upper bound of 6 cm is $6.4\dot{9}$ (ie 6.49999999...), so we should be writing:

     $5.5 \leq 6 < 6.5$ (*note the two different symbols*)

It's also important to realise that the number 6.0 implies a greater accuracy:

     $5.95 \leq 6.0 < 6.05$

In other words, 6 and 6.0 are different numbers when you consider the range of values each represents.

Questions often ask you to answer to a particular number of *significant figures* or *decimal places*. The first significant figure is the first non-zero digit. The first decimal place is the first figure after the decimal point. Try these:

     Write the following numbers to 3SF: 41.26, 2096, 21.04, 699.8

     Write the following numbers to 1DP: 12.392, 0.061, 4.952

Answers

41.3, 2100, 21.0, 700

12.4, 0.1, 5.0

But when you are working through a calculation, you should *not* round off at intermediate stages. Keep full calculator accuracy until you get to the answer, then round .

If you're not sure what negative powers mean, look ahead to the section on exponents, page 8.

If a question asks you to answer to a "suitable" degree of accuracy that usually means you should not be *too* accurate. For example, if a diagram gives lengths to 2SF, your answer should also be to 2SF.

Standard form: Standard form gives us an alternative way of writing very large and very small numbers without using lots of zeroes. For example:

     $43\,000 = 4.3 \times 10\,000 = 4.3 \times 10^4$

     $23\,000\,000 = 2.3 \times 10\,000\,000 = 2.3 \times 10^7$

     $0.000\,56 = \frac{5.6}{10\,000} = 5.6 \times \frac{1}{10\,000} = 5.6 \times 10^{-4}$

     $0.000\,000\,109 = \frac{1.09}{10\,000\,000} = 1.09 \times 10^{-7}$

Ordinary size numbers can also be written in standard form. For example, $12.5 = 1.25 \times 10^1$. Why would you want to do this? Sometimes calculations involving very big and very small numbers can end up as ordinary size numbers! For example:

     $(2.4 \times 10^8) \times (3 \times 10^{-9}) = 7.2 \times 10^{-1} = 0.72$

It is important that the first part of the number is between 1 and 10. If you do a calculation and the answer comes out as 12×10^4 this is not in standard form: it must be written as 1.2×10^5.

Some general points about standard form:

- A common mistake is to write eg 4.1×10^3 as 4.1^3
- Make sure you know how to enter numbers in standard form on your GDC, and also how to set the GDC to give answers in standard form. But be careful not to use "calculator notation"; for example, some calculators might display 3×10^{12} as 3E12.
- To add or subtract standard form numbers without a calculator, convert numbers back to ordinary form.
- In exam questions, you may be asked to "give your answer in the form $a \times 10^k$, where $1 \le a < 10$ and $k \in \mathbb{Z}$" – this is just a formal way of defining standard form.

1.3 Sequences and Series

There are many different types of number sequence. You only need to know about two: the *arithmetic sequence* (or *progression*) (AP) and the *geometric sequence* (GP). In an AP each number is the previous number **plus** a constant. In a GP each number is the previous number **multiplied** by a constant. A *series* is the same as a *sequence* except that the terms are added together: thus a series has a *sum*, whereas a sequence does not.

To answer most sequences and series questions, make sure you are familiar with the formulae below.

First, the notation:

u_1 = the first term of the sequence

n = the number of terms in the sequence

d = the common difference (the number added on in an AP)

r = the common ratio (the multiplier in a GP)

u_n = the value of the nth term

S_n = the sum of the first n terms

S_∞ = the sum to infinity

Try working out the values of d and r in the sequences in the examples box above.

Examples

Arithmetic sequences:

3, 5, 7, 9 ...

1.1, 1.3, 1.5, 1.7 ...

11, 7, 3, -1, -5 ...

Geometric sequences:

1, 3, 9, 27 ...

4, 6, 9, 13.5 ...

12, 6, 3, 1.5, 0.75 ...

2, -6, 18, -54 ...

Answers

d: 2, 0.2, -4

r: 3, 1.5, 0.5, -3

The formulae

For an AP:

The value of the nth term: $u_n = u_1 + (n-1)d$

$$d = u_{n+1} - u_n$$

The sum of n terms: $S_n = \frac{n}{2}(u_1 + u_n) = \frac{n}{2}(2u_1 + (n-1)d)$

The sum formulae always start from the first term. If you wanted to sum, say, the 10th term to the 20th term, you would calculate $S_{20} - S_9$. Think about it!

For a GP:

The value of the nth term: $u_n = u_1 r^{n-1}$

$$r = \frac{u_{n+1}}{u_n}$$

The sum of n terms: $S_n = \dfrac{u_1(r^n - 1)}{r - 1}$ or $\dfrac{u_1(1 - r^n)}{1 - r}$

And for GPs only there is a formula for "the sum to infinity." If the common ratio is in the range $-1 < r < 1$ then the terms get ever smaller and approach zero. In this case, the *sum* of the series will converge on a particular value. To calculate this value:

The sum to infinity: $S_\infty = \dfrac{u_1}{1 - r}$

Series questions often involve algebra as well as numbers. Note that to find d given two consecutive terms in an AP, subtract the first from the second; and to find r in a GP, divide the second by the first.

Example: A geometric series has first two terms 2 and k. What range of values of k will ensure the series converges?

Solution: The common ratio must be between -1 and 1. The common ratio is $\dfrac{k}{2}$ so

$-1 < \dfrac{k}{2} < 1 \;\Rightarrow\; -2 < k < 2.$

An arithmetic sequence has third term 12 and sixth term 18.

   (a)   Find the common difference.

   (b)   Find the first term.

   (c)   Find the sum of the first 11 terms.

Using the formula for nth term, we get:

$$u_3 = u_1 + 2d = 12$$
$$u_6 = u_1 + 5d = 18$$

(a)   Solving simultaneously, $3d = 6$ giving $d = 2$.

(b)   Substituting d into the first equation,

$$u_1 + 2 \times 2 = 12 \text{ giving } u_1 = 8.$$

(c) $S_{11} = \dfrac{11}{2}(2 \times 8 + (11 - 1) \times 2)$

$\qquad = \dfrac{11}{2}(16 + 20) = 11 \times 18 = 198$

Once we know the first term and the common difference, we can solve any further questions about the sequence.

You will sometimes find that questions use algebra to define a sequence or its terms. Here's an example where you are given successive *sums* of an AP and have to find the terms.

The trick here is that u_1 is the same as S_1, $u_2 = S_2 - S_1$ and so on.

Example: Successive sums of the terms of an arithmetic sequence are given by:
$S_1 = 1 + t,\; S_2 = 3 + 4t,\; S_3 = 6 + 9t$

Find the first two terms, common difference, and an expression for u_n.

Solution: $u_1 = 1 + t,\; u_2 = (3 + 4t) - (1 + t) = 2 + 3t$

$d = (2 + 3t) - (1 + t) = 1 + 2t$

Using the formula, $u_n = u_1 + (n - 1)d = (1 + t) + (n - 1)(1 + 2t)$

You can easily check the answer by substituting $n = 1$ and $n = 2$.

Multiply out and simplify to get $u_n = n + (2n - 1)t$

It often happens that, where formulae are involved, you are given the value of the variable on the left-hand side, and have to find the value of one of the other variables. This will always involve solving an equation, and the sequence and series formulae are no different in this respect from any others.

> (a) Find the number of terms in the geometric series $1 + 3 + 9 + 27 + \ldots + 59\,049$
>
> (b) Calculate the sum of the series in part (a).

| a) $u_n = u_1 r^{n-1}$
 $59\,049 = 1 \times 3^{n-1}$
 $n = 11$
 b) $S_n = \dfrac{u_1(r^n - 1)}{r - 1}$
 $S_{11} = \dfrac{1(3^{11} - 1)}{3 - 1} = 88\,573$ | *(a) We want to know the value of n for which $u_n = 59\,049$. We know the first term, the common ratio is clearly 3, so we just substitute these values into the relevant formula. It's good practice to write down any formula you're going to use – apart from anything else, it helps you to substitute values accurately.*

 We can solve this equation using logs, trial and error, or using the solve function on the GDC. |

Remember that the common difference and the common ratio can also be negative:

AP with $u_1 = 7$ and $d = -2$: $7, 5, 3, 1, -1, -3 \ldots$

GP with $u_1 = 2$ and $r = -1.5$: $2, -3, 4.5, -6.75 \ldots$

> Find the sum of the infinite geometric series $\dfrac{3}{5} - \dfrac{9}{20} + \dfrac{27}{80} - \dfrac{81}{320} + \ldots$

$\text{Sum} = \dfrac{a}{1 - r} = \dfrac{^3\!/_5}{^7\!/_4} = \dfrac{12}{35}$

Ways of defining sequences and series: Other than listing the numbers, there are two methods for defining a sequence:

- *Function definition*, eg $u_n = 2n^2 + 1$, giving $3, 9, 19, 33 \ldots$

- *Recursive definition*, eg $u_1 = 5,\ u_{n+1} = 1 + \dfrac{1}{u_n}$ giving $\dfrac{6}{5}, \dfrac{11}{6}, \dfrac{17}{11}$

> Note that neither of these sequences is an AP or a GP. *Any* set of numbers forms a sequence.

Sigma notation can be used to turn the function definition of a sequence into a series; in other words, where the terms of the sequence are added together. In the following example, the sigma symbol means "the sum of."

- *Sigma notation*, $\displaystyle\sum_{1}^{4}(k^2 - 2) = (1^2 - 2) + (2^2 - 2) + (3^2 - 2) + (4^2 - 2) = 22$

Example: Given that $\displaystyle\sum_{k=1}^{k=n}(4k - 1) = 1176$, find the value of n.

Solution: The series begins $3 + 7 + 11 + 15$, so we are dealing with an AP with $u_1 = 3$ and $d = 4$.

> Full working can be found on the website

Using the sum formula, $1176 = \dfrac{n}{2}(6 + (n - 1)4)$. This multiplies out to give a quadratic equation with solution $n = 24$.

Sequences and Series: Practice Exercise

These questions give you some practice in the basics – they are not intended to be the equivalent of exam-style questions.

Answers

1. 48, 1452
2. 39366, 531440
3. 3
4. 9
5. 16
6. 4, –1
7. –22
8. $\sum_{1}^{100}(3k-2)$

1. Find the 10th term and the sum of the first 24 terms of the sequence which begins 3, 8, 13, 18 …

2. Find the 10th term and the sum of the first 12 terms of the sequence which begins 2, 6, 18, 54 …

3. A geometric series has first term 3.5 and sum to 10 terms 103 334. Find the common ratio.

4. In an arithmetic sequence the first term is 3 and the sixth term is four times greater than the second term. Find the common difference.

5. In a geometric series, the first term is 0.4 and the common ratio is 2.5. Find the least value of n such that $S_n > 300\,000$.

   Not the easiest of questions – perhaps use the table functionality of your GDC?

6. A sequence is defined by $u_n = an + b$. Given that $u_1 = 3$ and $S_3 = 21$, find the values of a and b.

7. Find the value of $\sum_{k=1}^{k=5}(-1)^k 2^k$.

8. Express the series $1 + 4 + 7 + 10 + \ldots + 298$ in the form $\sum_{1}^{n} f(k)$.

1.4 Sequences and Series: Applications

One important application of sequences and series is their use in solving financial problems involving interest. If a sum of money is invested, the interest is the amount (expressed as a %) that it earns during each period (usually, but not necessarily, a year).

It is important to remember the single calculations which will:

- Find a percentage of an amount
- Increase or decrease an amount by a percentage

  5 % of 650 = 0.05 × 650

  12 % of 2000 = 0.12 × 2000

  Increase 120 by 5 % = 120 × 1.05

  Increase 4500 by 12 % = 4500 × 1.12

  Decrease 55 by 2 % = 55 × 0.98

Simple interest: the interest earned is not added to the total amount which thus stays constant.

- $1000 at 5% simple interest per year will earn $50/year.

  In 10 years, the investment is worth 1000 + 10 × 50 = $1500.

Compound interest: the interest earned is added to the amount invested. Thus the investment grows by a larger amount each year.

- $1000 at 5% compound interest will multiply by 1.05 each year

  After 1 year, the investment is worth 1000 × 1.05 = $1050

  After 2 years, the investment is worth 1050 × 1.05^2 = $1102.50

  After n years, the investment is worth 1000×1.05^n

Note that with simple interest, the value of the investment is increased by $50 each year and will form an AP. With compound interest, the value will multiply by 1.05 each year and will form a GP.

Beware of questions where extra money is added to the investment each year *as well as* the interest.

Mary invested $2000 for 4 years at 3% simple interest. Mo invested $2000 for 3 years at 4% compound interest. Which investment was then worth more?	
Mary: 3% of $2000 = $60. So after 4 years Mary's investment was worth $2240. **Mo:** After 3 years Mo's investment was worth $2000 \times 1.04^3 = \$2249.73$. Mo's investment was worth more.	*Sometimes a question asks how much interest the investment made. So in this case Mary's interest totalled $240. Mo's interest totalled $249.73.*

Sometimes a sneaky question uses a time period other than a year, but the calculations are done in the same way. If an investment attracts compound interest of 6% per annum, paid every month, then we can regard this as being the same as 0.5% per month. To find the value of an investment after 6 years, the multiplier would be 1.005^{72} (72 months at 0.5% per month).

⊞ Make sure you also know how to use the finance apps on your GDC

Depreciation: Investments attracting interest appreciate in value, whereas some items will lose value. For example, if a car was bought new for €13000 and then depreciated by 30% each year, after three years it would be worth $13000 \times 0.7^3 = €4459$. Radioactive decay provides another example of a decreasing quantity.

Example: A radioactive substance decays such that it loses 4% of its mass per year. After how many full years would 10 kg first reduce to less than 5 kg?

See the website for more detail about solving this inequality

Solution: We need to solve $10 \times 0.96^t < 5$, giving $t > 16.979...$ so $t = 17$ years.

The previous example showed a non-financial application. Here's another one. Note that the question doesn't mention sequences and series – you have to be alert to the fact that this is the area of the syllabus it relates to.

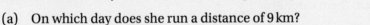

Each day a runner trains for a 9 km race. On the 1st day she runs 1000 m, and then increases the distance by 250 m on each subsequent day.	
(a) On which day does she run a distance of 9 km? (b) What is the total distance in km she will have run in training by the end of that day?	

| (a) $u_n = u_1 + (n-1)d$

 $9000 = 1000 + (n-1) \times 250$

 $8000 = 250n - 250$

 $\therefore \quad n = 33$ days

 (b) $S_n = \frac{n}{2}(u_1 + u_n)$

 $S_n = \frac{33}{2}(1000 + 9000) = 165\,000$

 She will have run $165\,000$ m = 165 km | *In part (a) we are dealing with the terms of an AP. We know the value of the last term, but need the number of terms. Notice that the question has distances in both km and m.*

 In part (b) we are looking for the sum of the series. It's easier to use the formula containing u_n (the last term) since we know it is 9000.

 Don't forget to convert back to km at the end. |

1.5 Exponents

What are exponents? *Exponent* is another word for power or index. You must understand the meaning of negative and fractional powers as well as positive, whole number powers. You must also be very familiar with the rules for using powers.

First, let's look at powers of 2:

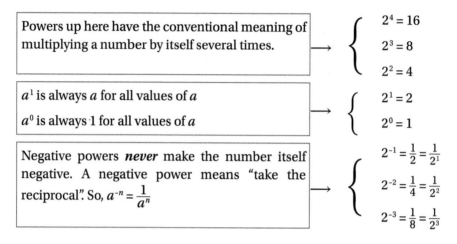

Powers up here have the conventional meaning of multiplying a number by itself several times.	$\longrightarrow$	$2^4 = 16$
		$2^3 = 8$
		$2^2 = 4$

| a^1 is always a for all values of a | $\longrightarrow$ | $2^1 = 2$ |
| a^0 is always 1 for all values of a | | $2^0 = 1$ |

Negative powers ***never*** make the number itself negative. A negative power means "take the reciprocal". So, $a^{-n} = \dfrac{1}{a^n}$	$\longrightarrow$	$2^{-1} = \dfrac{1}{2} = \dfrac{1}{2^1}$
		$2^{-2} = \dfrac{1}{4} = \dfrac{1}{2^2}$
		$2^{-3} = \dfrac{1}{8} = \dfrac{1}{2^3}$

Examples:

$2.5^1 = 2.5$

$4^{-2} = \dfrac{1}{16}$

$\left(\dfrac{2}{3}\right)^{-3} = \left(\dfrac{3^3}{2^3}\right) = \dfrac{27}{8}$

$8^{\frac{5}{3}} = \left(\sqrt[3]{8}\right)^5 = 32$

Fractional powers always involve *roots*.

Power	Meaning
$x^{\frac{1}{2}}$	$\sqrt{x}$
$x^{\frac{1}{3}}$	$\sqrt[3]{x}$
$x^{\frac{3}{2}}$	$\sqrt{x^3} = (\sqrt{x})^3$
$x^{-\frac{2}{5}}$	$\dfrac{1}{\sqrt[5]{x^2}}$

In general, $x^{\frac{1}{n}} = \sqrt[n]{x}$ and $x^{\frac{m}{n}} = \sqrt[n]{x^m} = \left(\sqrt[n]{x}\right)^m$.

Laws of exponents: The rules which follow occur in all sorts of mathematical situations and you should learn them carefully:

Examples

- $a^x \times a^y = a^{x+y}$ $2^{x+3} = 2^x \times 2^3 = 8 \times 2^x$
- $a^x \div a^y = a^{x-y}$ $\dfrac{x^3}{x^5} = x^{3-5} = x^{-2}$ or $\dfrac{1}{x^2}$
- $(a^x)^y = a^{xy}$ $9^x = (3^2)^x = 3^{2x}$
- $(ab)^x = a^x b^x$ $(3x)^3 = 3^3 \times x^3 = 27x^3$

Solving equations containing exponents: First, ensure that you are familiar with common powers of integers from 2 to 6.

$2^2 = 4,\ 2^3 = 8,\ 2^4 = 16,\ 2^5 = 32,\ 2^6 = 64,\ 2^7 = 128.$

$3^2 = 9,\ 3^3 = 27,\ 3^4 = 81,\ 3^5 = 243.$

$4^2 = 16,\ 4^3 = 64,\ 4^4 = 256.$

$5^2 = 25,\ 5^3 = 125,\ 5^4 = 625.$

$6^2 = 36,\ 6^3 = 216.$

You may literally need to know these backwards. For example, to solve $243 \times 3^{2x} = 1$ you would need to recognise that $243 = 3^5$ ($x = -2.5$).

Fractional powers always involve roots. In the non-calculator paper, the laws of exponents will help you to simplify expressions. For example, we can use $9 = 3^2$ to simplify $\dfrac{\sqrt{3} \times 9^{\frac{2}{3}}}{\sqrt[3]{9}}$.

$$\frac{\sqrt{3} \times 9^{\frac{2}{3}}}{\sqrt[3]{9}} = \frac{3^{\frac{1}{2}} \times (3^2)^{\frac{2}{3}}}{(3^2)^{\frac{1}{3}}} = \frac{3^{\frac{1}{2}} \times 3^{\frac{4}{3}}}{3^{\frac{2}{3}}} = \frac{3^{\frac{11}{6}}}{3^{\frac{2}{3}}} = 3^{\frac{7}{6}}$$

We can use a similar technique to solve an equation such as $4^x - 4 \times 8^x = 0$. The trick is to look for a common base, in this case 2.

$$(2^2)^x - 2^2 \times (2^3)^x = 0$$

$$2^{2x} = 2^{2+3x}$$

$$2x = 2 + 3x$$

$$x = -2$$

This one's a bit harder: $8^x = 0.25^{3x-1}$. Think of 0.25 as a fraction, and then convert it to a power of 2. The final answer is $x = \frac{2}{9}$.

Solve the equation $9x = 27^{1-x}$.	
$(3^2)^x = (3^3)^{1-x}$ $3^{2x} = 3^{3-3x}$ $2x = 3 - 3x$ $5x = 3$ $x = \dfrac{3}{5}$	*As in the previous examples, we need to use a common base. In this case it will be 3.* *The answer could also be given as 0.6. Fractions and decimals are different forms of the same number.*

The next exam-style question is obviously about exponents but, look carefully, and it's actually a quadratic equation. In other words, it's of the form something² + something + number. You will also find this form when dealing with trigonometric equations and equations involving e^x.

See page 31 and page 48

(a) Show that the equation $(2^x)^2 + 2^x - 20 = 0$ can be written in the form $(2^x + a)(2^x + b) = 0$, where a and b are integers to be found. (b) Hence solve the equation for x and explain why there is only one solution.	
(a) $\quad (2^x)^2 + 2^x - 20 = 0$ $\qquad y^2 + y - 20 = 0$ $\qquad (y + 5)(y - 4) = 0$ $\qquad (2^x + 5)(2^x - 4) = 0$ (b) So $2^x = -5$ or $2^x = 4$. But exponentials cannot take negative values, so the only solution is $2^x = 4$, giving $x = 2$.	*It may help to use y as the base of quadratic, then replace y with 2^x.* *When solving equations in exams, it's always a good idea to substitute your answer into the original equation to check you are right. In this case, with x = 2, we get* $\qquad 4^2 + 4 - 20 = 16 + 4 - 20 = 0$

1.6 Logarithms

Mapping $x \to 2^x$
gives
$3 \to 8$
$2 \to 4$
$1 \to 2$
$0 \to 1$
$-1 \to 0.5$
and $\log_2 x \gets x$

What is a logarithm? The mapping diagram in the notes box shows the function $f(x) = 2^x$ applied to a few integers. The inverse of this function would map $8 \to 3$, $4 \to 2$ and so on: in other words, it would find what power of 2 gives the required number. As shown at the bottom of the diagram, the inverse is the logarithm function. So the logarithm to the *base 2* of a number is the power of 2 which gives the number. For example, $\log_2 16 = 4$. It may be helpful to think of the relationship of the log(arithm) function to the power function as similar to that between the square root function and the square function.

Examples:

$\log_3 27 = 3$

$\log_{10} 0.1 = -1$

$\log_2(\sqrt{2}) = \frac{1}{2}$

$\log_5(5^x) = x$

Change of base: Logarithms can be to any base, and occasionally you may need to change from one base to another, in which case use the change of base formula:

$$\log_b a = \frac{\log_c a}{\log_c b}$$

For example: Simplify $\log_a 18 \times \log_3 a = \frac{\log_3 18}{\log_3 a} \times \log_3 a = \log_3 18$

Laws of logarithms: Because logarithms are just powers, the laws of logarithms are very similar to the laws of exponents. You should be very familiar with them, although you will find them in the formula book. These rules apply to logs with any base.

- $\log a + \log b = \log(ab)$
- $\log a - \log b = \log(a/b)$
- $\log a^n = n \log a$

The last gives a useful method for solving equations with powers in because it can be used to "bring the power down."

A common mistake is to write $\log a x^2$ as $2 \log a x$. This would only work if the square applied to the a as well. But we could also use the first law to get:

$\log a x^2 = \log a + \log x^2$

$= \log a + 2 \log x$

Example: Solve $2^x = 13$

The logs can be to any base, so in practice use the log key on your calculator (ie base 10).

$2^x = 13$

$\log(2^x) = \log 13$

$x \log 2 = \log 13$

$x = \frac{\log 13}{\log 2} = 3.70$

It's almost certain that you will get exam questions which involve the laws of logarithms. The following is typical:

If $\log_a 2 = x$ and $\log_a 5 = y$, find in terms of x and y expressions for (a) $\log_2 5$ and (b) $\log_a 20$	
(a) $\log_b a = \dfrac{\log_c a}{\log_c b}$ So $\log_2 5 = \dfrac{\log_a 5}{\log_a 2} = \dfrac{y}{x}$ (b) $20 = 5 \times 2^2$ So $\log_a 20 = \log_a(2^2 \times 5)$ $= \log_a 2^2 + \log_a 5$ $= 2\log_a 2 + \log_a 5$ $= 2x + y$	*We are given logs to the base a and, in part (a), we want a log to the base 2. It follows that we need to use the change of base formula.* *Don't get confused by the letters. The "a" in the formula is not the same "a" as in the question!* *In part (b) we need to rewrite 20 in terms of 2 and 5, without using addition or subtraction. We then use law 3 followed by law 1.*

Logarithms can crop up in all sorts of unlikely places. Examiners quite like including them in sequences and series questions.

Example: The first two terms of an infinite geometric series are $3\log_2 x$ and $\log_2 x$. Find the sum of the series.

Solution: We need the common ratio which is $\dfrac{u_2}{u_1} = \dfrac{\log_2 x}{3\log_2 x} = \dfrac{1}{3}$. Now we know it's an infinite sequence so the sum is $\dfrac{u_1}{1-r} = \dfrac{3\log_2 x}{1-\frac{1}{3}} = \dfrac{9\log_2 x}{2}$.

No need to use the laws of logarithms there. But how about this one?

Example: The first two terms of an arithmetic sequence are $\log_2 x$ and $\log_2\left(\frac{x}{4}\right)$. Find the common difference, giving your answer as an integer.

Solution: $d = u_2 - u_1 = \log_2\left(\frac{x}{4}\right) - \log_2 x = \log_2\left(\frac{x/4}{x}\right) = \log_2 \frac{1}{4} = -2$

Solving equations containing logarithms: You'll find that equations involving logs reduce to two main types:

$$\log_a(f(x)) = \log_a(g(x)) \text{ or } \log_a(f(x)) = b$$

eg: $\log_2 x + \log_2 5 = \log_2(x+1) \;\Rightarrow\; 5x = x+1 \;\Rightarrow\; x = \frac{1}{4}$

eg: $\log_3 x - \log_3 6 = 2 \;\Rightarrow\; \log_3\left(\frac{x}{6}\right) = 2 \;\Rightarrow\; \frac{x}{6} = 3^2 \;\Rightarrow\; x = 54$

I can't emphasise too much how important it is to know the laws of exponents and logarithms by heart so that you can easily apply them in a variety of mathematical situations. Also, be absolutely clear what a logarithm is, and understand that $\log_b x = y$ is the same as $x = b^y$.

Logarithms: Practice Exercise

Try the following questions if you require more practice in the basic manipulation of logarithms. Only number 7 needs a GDC.

1. Solve $\log_5 x + \log_5 3 = \log_5 12$

2. Solve $\log_4 p = 3$

3. Rewrite $\log_{10} 3 + 2\log_{10} 5$ as a single logarithm

4. Find the exact value of x (in terms of a) in the equation $\log_a(2x-1) = 3$

5. If $\log_3 a = m$ and $\log_3 b = n$, write $\log_3\left(\frac{\sqrt{a}}{b}\right)$ in terms of m and n

6. Let $\log_b 2 = p$ and $\log_b 5 = q$. Find an expression in terms of p and q for:

    (i) $\log_b 10$

    (ii) $\log_b 50$

7. Solve $\log_9 4 + \log_3 x = 3$

8. Find the value of b if $\log_b 7 = \frac{1}{2}$

9. Use logarithms to solve $4^{2x+1} = 100$

▣ See video online for the solution of $\log_6 x + \log_6(x-5) = 2$, $x>0$

Answers

1. 4
2. 64
3. $\log_{10} 75$
4. $\dfrac{a^3+1}{2}$
5. $\frac{1}{2}m - n$
6. (i) $p+q$
   (ii) $p+2q$
7. 1.161...
8. 49
9. 1.16 to 3SF

Question 4 is a more complicated form of question 2.

In question 5, first use law 2 then law 3.

In question 7, use the change of base formula to rewrite the first log using logs to base 3.

11

1.7 The Binomial Expansion

Calculation of binomial coefficients: It is helpful to remember the first few rows of Pascal's Triangle; the blue numbers in the table are called "binomial coefficients." For example, the 5th row, 3rd column is $^5C_3 = 10$.

	0th	1st	2nd	3rd	4th	5th
1st	1	1				
2nd	1	2	1			
3rd	1	3	3	1		
4th	1	4	6	4	1	
5th	1	5	10	10	5	1

Each number can also be calculated using the combinatorial formula:

$$^nC_r = \frac{n!}{r!(n-r)!}$$

For example,
$4! = 4 \times 3 \times 2 \times 1$

Thus, $^5C_3 = \frac{5!}{3!(5-3)!} = \frac{5!}{3!2!} = \frac{120}{6 \times 2} = 10$

With larger numbers it is helpful to write the factorials out so that you can see what cancels top and bottom. For example:

$$^7C_4 = \frac{7!}{4!3!} = \frac{7 \times 6 \times 5 \times 4 \times 3 \times 2 \times 1}{(4 \times 3 \times 2 \times 1)(3 \times 2 \times 1)} = \frac{7 \times 6 \times 5}{3 \times 2 \times 1} = 7 \times 5 = 35$$

The cancelling is important because otherwise you would find yourself trying to calculate 7! – not advisable when you're doing an exam! So you will **always** be able to cancel the larger factorial on the bottom with the right hand part of the factorial on the top. In the example above, I then calculated the bottom line as 6, and cancelled this with the 6 in the top line.

With a bit of practice, you shouldn't have to write out the factorials at all.

So in this example, I have cancelled the 7! on the bottom with most of the 9! on the top.

$$^9C_2 = \frac{9 \times 8}{2 \times 1} = 36$$

Without a calculator, work out the values of:

$$^6C_3, \,^9C_1, \,^8C_5, \,^4C_2 \qquad (20, 9, 56, 6)$$

 You should also be able to use your GDC to calculate a single binomial coefficient (using the ^nC_r formula); and a set of binomial coefficients, equivalent to a single row in the table above. There are a couple of ways this can be achieved:

Using a table: To return, say, the 6th row, set up the function $6\,^nC_r\,x$ (different calculators will do this in different ways), and then look at the table of values where x starts at 0 and increments in steps of 1. Clearly there is no meaning to the values returned when $x > 6$.

Using a list: To return the 6th row, enter $6\,^nC_r\{0, 1, 2, 3, 4, 5, 6\}$ where the curly brackets indicate a list of vales. This will then return another list containing the binomial coefficients.

The Binomial Expansion: The general formula gives you a quick way of multiplying out brackets of the form $(a + b)^n$ where n is a natural number. It is best illustrated with an example.

To expand $(a + b)^4$ each term will have 3 parts to it: the appropriate Pascal's Triangle number (in this case using row 4), a to a power beginning at 4 and reducing to 0, b to a power beginning at 0 and increasing to 4. The 1s that result in the first and last terms reduce those terms to a^4 and b^4.

$$(a + b)^4 = a^4 + 4a^3b + 6a^2b^2 + 4ab^3 + b^4$$

This general form can now be used to expand more specific expressions, for example $(2 - 3x)^4$. When doing this, note:

- Always write out the general form first, then substitute underneath (in this case, $a = 2$, $b = -3x$).
- Use brackets throughout to ensure correct calculation.
- Use one line to substitute, the next (possibly more than one) to calculate.

$$(2 - 3x)^4 = 2^4 + 4(2)^3(-3x) + 6(2)^2(-3x)^2 + 4(2)(-3x)^3 + (-3x)^4$$

$$= 16 - 96x + 216x^2 - 216x^3 + 81x^4$$

Be careful when substituting a negative number – always use brackets.

Use binomial expansion to express $(1 + \sqrt{7})^3$ in the form $p + q\sqrt{7}$, $p, q \in \mathbb{Z}$	
$(a + b)^3 = a^3 + 3a^2b + 3ab^2 + b^3$ $(1 + \sqrt{7})^3 = 1^3 + 3 \times 1^2 \times (\sqrt{7}) + 3 \times 1 \times (\sqrt{7})^2 + (\sqrt{7})^3$ $= 1 + 3\sqrt{7} + 21 + 7\sqrt{7}$ $= 22 + 10\sqrt{7}$	*Ability to manipulate surds (expressions with square roots) comes under "prior knowledge" in the syllabus*

Finding individual terms: It is often the case that, in an exam question, you are asked to find a specific term rather than the whole expansion. For example, let's find the term in x^3 in the expansion of $(2 - \frac{1}{2}x)^7$. We need to work out the three constituent parts of the term:

- The binomial coefficient is $^7C_3 = 35$
- The power of the x part is 3, so this gives $(-\frac{1}{2}x)^3 = -\frac{1}{8}x^3$
- The powers always add to give the overall power, so the third part is $2^4 = 16$

Thus the overall term is $35 \times 16 \times (-\frac{1}{8}x^3) = -70x^3$

A common problem is to find the "constant term"; that is, the term which is just a number. In other words, it is the term which contains x^0. Watch the video solution for the following question and this will give you a general method.

Find the constant term in the expansion of $\left(2x - \dfrac{1}{x^2}\right)^9$	
Constant term $= -5376$	

Try the following examples for some extra practice:

1. Find the coefficient of x^2 in the expansion of $(2x - 3)^5$.

2. The coefficient of the x^2 term in the expansion of $(2 + ax)^{10}$ is $103\,680$. Find a.

3. Find the constant term in the expansion of $\left(2x^2 + \dfrac{4}{x}\right)^{12}$ in the form $^{12}C_r \times 4^k$, $k \in \mathbb{Z}$

Answers

-1080; 3; $^{12}C_8 \times 4^{10}$

1.8 Deductive proof

Equality and identity: We often use an "equals" sign rather sloppily. Consider the following two statements:

$3(x - 2) = 2x$ (1)

$3(x - 2) = 3x - 6$ (2)

Statement 1 is an *equation* and we are looking for solutions. In this case the only solution is $x = 6$. In other words, LHS and RHS will only be equal when $x = 6$. Statement 2 is an *identity*. The two expressions always have the same value whatever the value of x: they are just different ways of writing the same thing. Identities should always be written using the appropriate symbol which is $\equiv$.

$$3(x - 2) \equiv 3x - 6$$

LHS to RHS proof: Deductive proof is often called LHS to RHS proof to underline the fact that we must work *from* the LHS, ending up with the RHS. Solving an equation can be carried out by performing the same operations on both sides of the equation. You can't do this to prove an identity because you would need to start with the thing you are trying to prove! To take a simple example, let's prove $-1 = 1$.

Suppose $\qquad\qquad -1 = 1$

Square both sides: $\quad (-1)^2 = 1^2$

$$1 = 1$$

Since LHS = RHS, the original statement must be true!

This doesn't work because the algebra isn't necessarily reversible. Because $x^2 = y^2$ it doesn't follow that $x = y$.

So, never start a deductive proof by writing down what you want to prove – always start with *just* the LHS.

Example: Show that $(x - 2)^2 - 5 \equiv x^2 - 4x - 1$

Solution: $(x - 2)^2 - 5 \equiv x^2 - 4x + 4 - 5$

$$\equiv x^2 - 4x - 1 \qquad \text{qed}$$

When asked to prove conjectures involving numbers, remember that an even number is always of the form $2k$, and an odd number of the form $2k + 1$. For example, here is a proof that the sum of the squares of two consecutive integers is always an odd number:

Let the two integers be n and $n + 1$.

The sum of the squares $= n^2 + (n + 1)^2$

$$= n^2 + n^2 + 2n + 1$$

$$= 2n^2 + 2n + 1$$

$$= 2(n^2 + n) + 1$$

This is of the form $2k + 1$ and so is always odd.

(a) Show that $\dfrac{1}{m - 1} + \dfrac{1}{m^2 - m} \equiv \dfrac{m + 1}{m^2 - m}$

(b) Show that the identity is valid when $m = 2$

(a) $\dfrac{1}{m - 1} + \dfrac{1}{m^2 - m} \equiv \dfrac{1}{m - 1} + \dfrac{1}{m(m - 1)}$

$$\equiv \dfrac{m}{m(m - 1)} + \dfrac{1}{m(m - 1)}$$

$$\equiv \dfrac{m + 1}{m(m - 1)}$$

$$\equiv \dfrac{m + 1}{m^2 - m} \qquad \text{qed}$$

Make sure you know how to deal with algebraic fractions. As with numerical fractions, it is likely that you will need to find a common denominator.

(b) When $m = 2$, $\quad$ LHS $= \frac{1}{1} + \frac{1}{2} = \frac{3}{2}$ $\quad$ RHS $= \frac{3}{4-2} = \frac{3}{2}$ $\quad \therefore$ LHS = RHS	

A triangle has sides $\sqrt{2n+1}$, n and $n+1$, where $n+1$ is the longest side. Prove that the triangle is right-angled for any value of n.

We need to show that $(\sqrt{2n+1})^2 + n^2 \equiv (n+1)^2$ $\quad (\sqrt{2n+1})^2 + n^2 \equiv 2n + 1 + n^2$ $\qquad\qquad\qquad \equiv n^2 + 2n + 1$ $\qquad\qquad\qquad \equiv (n+1)(n+1)$ $\qquad\qquad\qquad \equiv (n+1)^2$ $\therefore$ The triangle is right-angled	*Right-angled triangle? Let's use Pythagoras' Theorem.* *There is a temptation to multiply out the RHS, but in LHS to RHS proofs you should work on the LHS only – unless you really can't see any way to get to the RHS unless you perform algebra on it as well.* *Note that I finished with the statement we were asked to prove*

Deductive proof: Practice Exercise

Here's a variety of proof questions. I suggest that in each case you also try substituting a value and show that LHS = RHS for that value.

1. Prove that $(n+1)^2 - (n-1)^2 \equiv 4n$

2. Prove that $\dfrac{x^2 + x}{x^2 + 4x + 3} \equiv \dfrac{x}{x+3}$

3. Given that k is any integer write down, in terms of k, three consecutive integers. Hence show that the sum of three consecutive integers is always a multiple of 3.

4. The nth term in the sequence of triangle numbers 1, 3, 6, 10, ...is given by $\frac{1}{2}n(n+1)$. Prove that 8 times any triangle number is always 1 less than a square number.

Number and Algebra: Long Answer Questions

Here's a selection of section B style exam questions related to the Number and Algebra topic, although some of them may require knowledge and techniques from other areas of the syllabus. The answers are given here, but full working may be found on the Peak Study Resources website.

See www.peakib.com

1. The first three terms of an infinite geometric sequence are $a - 1, 4, a + 5$, where $a \in \mathbb{Z}$.

    (a) (i)   Write down two expressions in terms of a for the common ratio r.

    (ii) Hence show that a satisfies the equation $a^2 + 4a - 21 = 0$.

    (iii) Solve the equation in (ii) to find the possible values of a.

    (iv) Hence find the possible values of r.

    The sequence has a finite sum.

    (b) (i)   State the value of r, justifying your answer.

    (ii) Calculate the sum of the sequence.

    _____

    Answers:

    (a) (i) $r = \dfrac{4}{a - 1}$ or $\dfrac{a + 5}{4}$

    (iii) $a = -7$ or 3

    (iv) $r = -\dfrac{1}{2}$ or 2

    (b) (i) $r = -\dfrac{1}{2}$ because $|r| < 1$

    (ii) $-\dfrac{16}{3}$

2. Let $f(x) = \log_2 2x + \log_2 12 - \log_2 6$, for $x > 0$

    a) (i)   Show that $f(x) = \log_2 4x$

    (ii) Find the value of $f(0.25)$ and $f(8)$

    (iii) Show that the function f can be written in the form $\dfrac{\ln ax}{\ln b}$ $a, b \in \mathbb{Z}$ where the values of a and b are to be found.

    b) (i)   Solve the equation $x^2 - 4x - 5 = 0$

    (ii) Show that $e^x - \dfrac{5}{e^x} = 4$ can be written as $e^{2x} - 4e^x - 5 = 0$

    (iii) Use your answers to parts (i) and (ii) to write down two values for e^x and explain why only one of them is valid.

    (iv) Hence write down the value of x in the form $\ln k, \ k \in \mathbb{Z}$

    _____

    Answers:

    (a) (ii) $0, 5$

    (iii) $a = 4, b = 2$

    (b) (i) $x = 5$ or -1

    (iii) $e^x = 5$ or $e^x = -1$. Only 5 is valid since $e^x > 0$

    (iv) $\ln 5$

3. (a) Given that $(x + 2)^4 \equiv x^4 + 8x^3 + Ax^2 + Bx + 16$

   (i) Find the values of A and B.

   (ii) Write down the expansion of $(x - 2)^4$

   (iii) Hence show that $(x + 2)^4 - (x - 2)^4 \equiv 16x(x^2 + 4)$

   (b) Use your answer to (a)(i) to find the term in x^2 in $(x + 2)^4\left(1 + \frac{1}{x^2}\right)$.

   _____

   Answers:

   (a) (i) $A = 24, B = 32$

   (ii) $x^4 - 8x^3 + 24x^2 - 32x + 16$

   (b) $25x^2$

4. a) (i) Prove that $(x + 2)^2 - 3 \equiv x^2 + 4x + 1$

   (ii) By multiplying both sides of the identity by $(x + 2)$, show that $(x + 2)^3 - 3(x + 2) = x^3 + ax^2 + 9x + b$, $a, b \in \mathbb{Z}$ where a and b are to be found.

   (iii) Hence show that $(x + 2)^3 \equiv x^3 + 6x^2 + 12x + 8$

   (iv) Show that the binomial expansion $(x + 2)^3$ gives the same result as in part (iii).

   b) (i) Find an expression for u_n for the sequence 1, 3, 5, 7 ......

   (ii) Hence show that the product of any two consecutive odd numbers is itself odd.

   _____

   Answers:

   (a) (ii) $a = 6, b = 2$

   (b) (i) $u_n = 2n - 1$

Chapter 2: FUNCTIONS

2.1 Basics of Functions

A function is an algebraic rule which shows how one set of numbers is related to, or obtained from another set. Functions often model real-life situations, so it is necessary to understand the notation used and the different types of function which may be used.

Defining functions: A function is defined using the notation $f(x)$, but note that other letters may be used, particularly if modelling physical quantities. For example, the velocity of an object at a particular time may be defined using $v(t)$; the cost of buying a number of articles could be given by $C(n)$.

Thus the function $f(x) = 3x^2 - 1$ can be read as: "Function f takes any number, x, and turns it into $3x^2 - 1$." The function notation is also used with specific numbers; for example, $f(2) = 3 \times 2^2 - 1 = 11$.

Domain: The set of values to be input to a function is called the domain. In many functions, any value can be input, in which case the domain is $x \in \mathbb{R}$. However, the domain may be restricted for two reasons:

- Certain values of x may give impossible results, such as division by 0 or the square root of a negative number. For example, x cannot take the value 4 in the function $f(x) = \dfrac{x}{x-4}$, and this would be written as: $f(x) = \dfrac{x}{x-4}$ for $x \neq 4$.

- For the purposes of a particular question the domain may be "artificially" restricted. If $g(x) = 2x^2 - 3$ for $x > 0$, the function would only take positive values of x.

It's important to note the domain in an exam question because it may affect your answer. Solving $g(x) = 5$ in the example above would lead to the solution $x^2 = 4$ and hence $x = 2$; $x = -2$ is not in the domain.

Range: The set of values produced by a function is called the range. In the examples above, the range of g is $g(x) > -3$ since there is a minimum at $(0, -3)$. The range of f is best found by inspecting a graph: the range is the complete set of possible y values, so in this case would be $f(x) \neq 1$.

> If you draw the graph of f you will see there is a horizontal asymptote at $y = 1$. All other y values are represented on the graph.

The next sections use the image of a "function machine" which represents a function as a black box.

When the handle is turned, the 5 drops in the top and the function machine turns it into an 11!

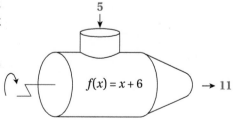

Inverse functions: An inverse function "reverses" the effect of a function. The inverse of add 2 is subtract 2. The inverse of squaring is square rooting. In terms of the function machine, just turn the handle the other way and the 11 turns back into a 5. The notation for an inverse function is $f^{-1}(x)$.

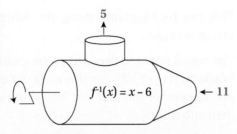

To work out the inverse of a function – particularly a more complex one – the method is:

- Write the function in the form y = the function
- Replace the 'y' with an 'x' and all the 'x's with 'y's.
- Make y the subject – you will have the inverse function.
- Write down the inverse function starting with $f^{-1}(x)$

A few points about inverse functions which you need to know:

- The graph of an inverse function can be found by reflecting the graph of the function in the line $y = x$.
- The statement $f(5) = 11$ is exactly the same as $f^{-1}(11) = 5$.
- The domain of a function is the same as the range of its inverse, and the range of a function is the same as the domain of its inverse.
- $(f \circ f^{-1})(x) = (f^{-1} \circ f)(x) = x$ (eg: $\sqrt{x^2} = (\sqrt{x})^2 = x$)

Example: Given that $f^{-1}(-8) = 3$, find the value of a in the function $f(x) = 10 - ax^2$.

Solution: If $f^{-1}(-8) = 3$ then it follows that $f(3) = -8$.

   Thus, $10 - a \times 3^2 = -8$ giving $a = 2$.

Given the function $f(x) = \sqrt{x+2}$ for $x \geq -2$,

   (a)   Find the inverse function $f^{-1}(x)$
   (b)   Find the domain of f^{-1}

(a) $y = \sqrt{x+2}$	a) *Use the steps above to find the inverse.*
$\quad x = \sqrt{y+2}$	*Note that the algebra is sometimes more*
$\quad x^2 = y + 2$	*complicated. For example, try finding the*
$\quad y = x^2 - 2$	*inverse of $f(x) = \frac{x+3}{2x-1}$.*
$\quad$ So $f^{-1}(x) = x^2 - 2$	
(b) Domain of f^{-1} is $x \geq 0$	b) *Domain of inverse = range of function.*

See the website for full working of the inverse example

Composite functions: If the values of one function are input to another one, the result is a composite function. Given $f(x) = x^2$ and $g(x) = x - 1$, then $f(g(3)) = f(2) = 4$. This is not the same as $g(f(3)) = g(9) = 8$. It is important to understand that the functions are not being multiplied together; a number is being put through one function, then the other.

Note that:
$(f^{-1} \circ f)(x) = (f \circ f^{-1})(x) = x$

This can be illustrated using the function machines again.

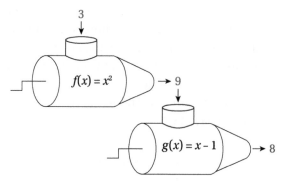

The actual notation used (to avoid multiple brackets) is $(g \circ f)(3)$. Say this as "g of f of 3" and remember that 3 is put into f first and then into g.

To find $(g \circ f)(x)$, work like this:
$(g \circ f)(x) = g(f(x)) = g(x^2)$. Now, in words, function g is "subtract 1." So $g(x^2) = x^2 - 1$.

Try using the same method to show that $(f \circ g)(x) = (x - 1)^2$.

Questions may also involve composites such as $f \circ f$ (put the value through function f twice), or $f^{-1} \circ g$ (put the value through function g then through the inverse of function f). Try the following examples:

$f(x) = 3x^2$, $g(x) = \frac{1}{x}$, find $(g \circ f)(x)$	$\dfrac{1}{3x^2}$
$f(x) = x^2$, $g(x) = \sin x$, find $(f \circ g)\left(\frac{2\pi}{3}\right)$	$\dfrac{3}{4}$
$f(x) = x + 4$, $g(x) = e^x$, find $(g^{-1} \circ f)(x)$	$\ln(x + 4)$
$f(x) = x + 1$, find $(f \circ f)(x)$	$x + 2$
$f(x) = x + 3$, $g(x) = 2^x$, solve $(f \circ g)(x) = (g \circ f)(x)$	-1.22 (GDC)

Given that $f(x) = 4(x - 1)$ and $g(x) = \dfrac{6 - x}{2}$

   (a)   Find g^{-1}

   (b)   Solve $(f \circ g^{-1})(x) = 4$

a) $y = \dfrac{6 - x}{2}$

      $x = \dfrac{6 - y}{2}$

      $2x = 6 - y$

      $y = 6 - 2x$

So $g^{-1}(x) = 6 - 2x$

b) $f(g^{-1}(x)) = 4$

      $f(6 - 2x) = 4$

      $4(6 - 2x - 1) = 4$

      $6 - 2x - 1 = 1$

      $2x = 4$

      $x = 2$

b) Just to reiterate – do not multiply the functions together. Put one function as the input to the second.

The following section looks in detail at all aspects of graphs

Using a graph to answer function questions: A graph is effectively a "picture" of a function. The x-axis contains the numbers input to the function and therefore represents the domain; the y-axis contains the resulting function values, and therefore shows the range. Thus a point with coordinates (a, b) is the graphical equivalent of $f(a) = b$, and also $f^{-1}(b) = a$. For example, the graph of $y = 2^x$ is a "picture" of the function $f(x) = 2^x$, and the point $(3, 8)$ represents $f(3) = 8$. It is helpful to think of the y-axis as the "function axis".

You can answer questions about a function just from its graph, even without an equation. For example, look at this graph. Because there is a point (5, 3), we know that $f(5) = 3$. What about $f^{-1}(-1)$? Work backwards from –1 on the y-axis, and we can see that $f^{-1}(-1) = -3$. Here are some more possible questions:

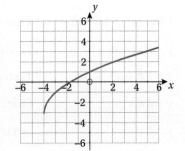

Find $(f \circ f)(-4)$.   Answer: $(f \circ f)(-4) = f(-3) = -1$

Solve $f^{-1}(a) = 0$.   Answer: $a = f(0) = 1$

What is the domain of f^{-1}?   Answer: same as the range of f, so $-3 \leq x \leq 3$

You may also be asked to sketch the graph of the inverse function. The easiest way to do this is to take key points, such as (5, 3), (2, 2), (0, 1), (–3, –1), (–4, –3) reverse their coordinates – (3, 5), (2, 2), (1, 0) etc – plot them and join them up.

2.2 Graphs of Functions

A graph is an excellent tool for interpreting a function. From a graph we can see when the function is increasing or decreasing, what the range of the function is, where it cuts the axes and so on. Therefore it is important to be able to sketch and understand graphs of different types of functions. Remember that your calculator can be of great benefit, and you should fully understand its graphing functions (see page 23); but you must also be able to sketch graphs without a calculator.

> Note the difference between "draw" and "sketch". Drawing a graph will require plotting many points. A sketch shows the shape of a graph and how it relates to the axes, with a few key points marked in.

Asymptotes: A graph such as $y = 2^x$ has a horizontal asymptote because as x gets smaller, the values of y get ever closer to 0 without ever reaching it. Some functions have graphs with vertical asymptotes which arise because division by 0 is impossible.

For example, $y = \dfrac{x}{2-x}$ (pictured) has a vertical asymptote at $x = 2$; as x gets closer to 2, the denominator gets closer to 0. This graph also has a horizontal asymptote at $y = -1$. Try putting x values of 10, 100 and 1000 into the function to see why.

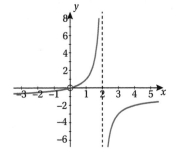

Significant features: The other main features of a graph you should be able to identify are the x-intercepts (where $y = 0$); the y-intercept (where $x = 0$); and turning points, where the gradient = 0. But note that a graph doesn't necessarily have all, or even any, of these features.

Transformations of graphs: You should be able to sketch the graphs of the basic functions $y = x^2$, $y = x^3$, $y = \frac{1}{x}$, $y = a^x$, $y = \log_b x$. The effect of simple numerical changes to these functions (involving additions, multiplications and minus signs) results in specific, simple transformations, thus extending the number of functions which can be easily sketched.

The graph transformations you need to know are:

Change to function	Transformation
$y = f(x) + a$	Translate (slide) graph upwards by a units
$y = f(x + a)$	Translate graph to the *left* by a units
$y = af(x)$	Stretch graph vertically by scale factor a
$y = f(ax)$	Stretch graph horizontally by scale factor $1/a$
$y = -f(x)$	Reflect graph in x-axis
$y = f(-x)$	Reflect graph in y-axis

Transformations in the x direction always do the opposite of what you expect!

For example, $y = (x - 1)^2 + 2$ will translate the graph of $y = x^2$ to the right by 1 and up by 2, that is, a translation of $\begin{pmatrix} 1 \\ 2 \end{pmatrix}$.

$y = -\dfrac{3}{x + 2}$ is a composite transformation of $y = \dfrac{1}{x}$. To obtain the correct order of transformations, consider what order you would work out the expression if you put in a value for x. This would be:

- Add 2 to x
- Multiply the function by 3
- Change sign

Be aware of the difference between, say, adding 2 to the x part of the function, and adding 2 to the *whole* function.

The equivalent transformations are:

- Translate left 2 units
- Stretch by 3 in the y direction
- Reflect in the x-axis

If a question asks you to sketch the transformation of a particular curve, the best way is to work out where the key points on the graph will move to, plot them, and then sketch the curve. And sometimes the transformation is not specifically mentioned.

On Paper 2 a GDC can be used for the first part; but because of the "hence" we must consider transformations for the second part.

Example: Find the turning point on the graph of $f(x) = x^2 + \dfrac{16}{x} - 9$ and hence write down the turning point on the graph of $f(x) = x^2 + \dfrac{16}{x}$.

Solution: Using differentiation, we find the turning point is when $x = 2$. Substitute this value into the function, and the turning point is $(2, 3)$. Now to get the second function we add 9 to the first, and so the graph has been translated up 9. The turning point goes with it, and is now at $(2, 12)$.

The graph of $f^{-1}(x)$: Consider the graph of $y = x^2$, $x > 0$ (which represents the function $f(x) = x^2$). When $x = 3$, $y = 9$ (ie $f(3) = 9$). The graph of the inverse function is $y = \sqrt{x}$, and when $x = 9$, $y = 3$. Any point (a, b) on the graph of f becomes (b, a) on the graph of f^{-1}. So the graph of $y = f^{-1}(x)$ is always the reflection of the graph of $y = f(x)$ in the line $y = x$.

Answers

1. $(2, 0), (-3, 0), (0, -6)$; $(2, 3), (-3, 3), (0, -3)$.

2. Translation $\begin{pmatrix} -3 \\ 0 \end{pmatrix}$ then stretch $\times 2$ in the y direction.

3. (a) $(0, 3), (-1, 4)$
   (b) $(-1, -3), (-3, -4)$

4. $(2, -1), a > 1$

Transformations of graphs: Practice exercise

1. Find the x-intercepts, y-intercept on the graph of $y = x^2 + x - 6$. Hence find the images of these points when transformed onto the graph of $y = x^2 + x - 3$.

2. The graph of $y = 2\ln x$ is obtained from the graph of $y = \ln(x - 3)$. List the transformations required.

3. The points (0, 3) and (–2, 4) lie on the graph of $f(x)$. Write down the equivalent points on the graphs of: (a) $f(2x)$; (b) $-f(x+1)$

4. Find the turning point on the graph of $f(x) = -x^2 + 4x - 5$. The graph of f is translated to the graph of g by the vector $\begin{pmatrix} 0 \\ a \end{pmatrix}$. Find the values of a such that $g(x) = 0$ has exactly two solutions.

☐ See the video online showing how to transform the graph of $f(x)$ using the transformation $2f(x-1)+2$

Functions and Graphs with a GDC

In this section of the syllabus, perhaps more than any other, you are expected to be able to use your graphic calculator for a wide range of techniques. Apart from using your GDC for calculations, two of its most important uses (as far as exams are concerned) are for drawing graphs and for solving equations.

Function keys: You should be able to enter a wide range of functions with confidence – you don't want to spend time in the exam searching your calculator. Look at the list in the notes box – make sure you can key in each of the functions. You should also be able to work in fraction notation, and be able to enter functions such as $y = \sqrt[3]{\dfrac{x}{x-1}}$.

$\sqrt[3]{12}$

$\cos^{-1} 0.867$

e^4

$\log_2 15$

Tables: GDCs have the facility to work out a table of values for a function. Having input the function in the form $y = f(x)$ you can set up a table by selecting the first x value and then the steps by which you want x to increase. In this example, the function $y = 2 - 3\sin x$ has been entered into the function editor, and then a table created starting with $x = 0$ and increasing x in steps of 30°. This can be helpful if you need to know several values, if you want to plot a graph by hand or if you're having difficulty creating the appropriate scales for a calculator plot – the table indicates the lowest and highest values of y and helps you set an appropriate window.

X	Y1
0	2
30	.5
60	-.5981
90	-1
120	-.5981
150	.5
180	2

X=0

Drawing graphs: Three important points to remember when drawing and using GDC graphs:

- Make sure the function you type into the editor is actually the same as in the question. You may, for example, have to use brackets which aren't actually required on the written page. 2^{x+3}, if typed as 2 ^ x + 3, will calculate as $2^x + 3$. To get the correct answer you would need a bracket: 2 ^ (x + 3).

Most modern calculators will allow the entry of expressions in their correct format, for example 2^{x+3} instead of 2^(x + 3). It is still important to ensure the correct use of brackets.

- The GDC has a few standard sets of scales, but you will probably have to set up the "window" yourself in order to see the required part of the graph. You may well have to zoom into a part of the graph to see exactly what is happening. The two screenshots are of the same graph, but only the lower one shows the intersections with the x-axis.

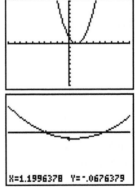

X=1.1996378   Y=-.0676379

- The GDC can give you the values of key points such as intersections with the axes, points where lines intersect, turning points and so on. If you want to read off your own point, make sure you know the scales being used, ie how much each mark on the axes is worth.

Solving equations: GDCs have built in equation solvers. However, if you already have the graph of the relevant function, then it can be used to solve equations. The easiest way to do this is to ensure your equation has a 0 on the right hand side because then all you have to do is find out where the graph cuts the axis. For example, solve $x^2 - 2 = \dfrac{1}{x}$, $x > 0$.

First we need to rewrite this equation as $x^2 - 2 - \frac{1}{x} = 0$ and draw the graph of $y = x^2 - 2 - \frac{1}{x}$.

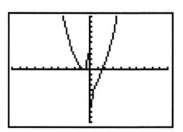

Now use the "zero" or "root" feature to find where the graph cuts the x-axis and this will be the solution to the equation which is $x = 1.618$.

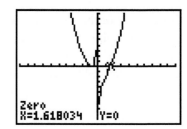

Given that $f(x) = x^3 \times 2^{-x}$, $x \geq 0$

    (a)   Sketch the graph of $f(x)$ showing its asymptotic behaviour.

    (b)   Find the co-ordinates of the maximum point, and hence state the range of $f(x)$.

    (c)   Draw a line on your graph to show that $f(x) = 1$ has two solutions.

    (d)   Find the solutions to $f(x) = 1$ giving your answers to 3 significant figures.

(a) and (c)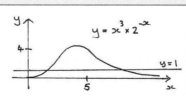

With a function like this we clearly need a calculator for the graph.

(a) When you sketch a graph, you must label the scales and the graph, and show at least one point on each axis to give an indication of scale. Do not go beyond the domain.

(b) Maximum = (4.33, 4.04)

     Range is $0 \leq f(x) \leq 4.04$

(c) The line $y = 1$ intersects $f(x)$ at two points.

(d) $x = 1.37$ or 9.94

(b) and (d) You should be able to use your GDC to find turning points on a graph, and to find where two graphs intersect.

They're called linear functions because they always give a straight line when drawn on a graph.

Formulae

The gradient between two points (x_1, y_1) and (x_2, y_2) is: $\frac{y_2 - y_1}{x_2 - x_1}$

Parallel lines: $m_1 = m_2$

Perpendicular lines: $m_1 = -\frac{1}{m_2}$

Midpoint of two points is: $\left(\frac{x_1 + x_2}{2}, \frac{y_1 + y_2}{2}\right)$

Distance between two points is: $\sqrt{(x_2 - x_1)^2 + (y_2 - y_1)^2}$

2.3 Linear Functions

In a linear function, the function increases (or decreases) at a constant rate. Its graph is a straight line.

Example: Cost of printing programmes against number of programmes printed.

Equation: $f(x) = ax + b$ where a and b are constants.

Gradient: The *gradient* of the line is its "steepness." A gradient of 3 means that y is increasing 3 times faster than x. The gradient is calculated by choosing two points and dividing the change in y by the change in x, often remembered as $\frac{\text{rise}}{\text{run}}$.

Horizontal lines have gradient 0. Vertical lines have an infinite gradient. Lines angled from bottom left to top right have positive gradients, others have negative gradients.

Midpoint, distance between two points: The midpoint of two points can be found by calculating the x-coordinate halfway between the x-coordinates of the two points, and the same for the y-coordinate. The distance between two points is calculated using Pythagoras' Theorem.

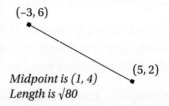

$(-3, 6)$

$(5, 2)$

Midpoint is (1, 4)
Length is $\sqrt{80}$

Although the formulae are shown in the box, this means there are a lot of formulae to remember. It is often better to draw a sketch and work from that.

Drawing a line from its equation:

- If the equation is of the form $y = mx + c$, substitute 2 or 3 values for x and work out the corresponding y values.

- If the equation is of the form $ax + by = c$, it is easier to put x equal to 0 and work out y, then put y equal to 0 and work out x. This gives the two points where the line crosses the axes.

- To *sketch* the graph of $y = mx + c$, remember that c is the y-intercept and m is the gradient.

> A useful line to remember is the one which passes through $(a, 0)$ and $(0, a)$. Its equation is $x + y = a$.

Working out the equation of a line from the graph:

1. Calculate the gradient.

There are two formulae you can use:

2a. If using the first formula, replace m with the gradient, then substitute a point for x and y.

$y = mx + c$

3a. Calculate c and then put this back into the equation.

2b. If using the second formula, replace m with the gradient then substitute the point for x_1 and y_1.

$y - y_1 = m(x - x_1)$

3b. Rearrange and simplify to get the equation.

The points P, Q have coordinates P(3, 0), Q(-3, 7). Find the equation of the line which is perpendicular to PQ and passes through P. Give your answer in the form $ax + by + c = 0$, where a, b and c are integers.

Gradient of PQ $= \dfrac{7 - 0}{-3 - 3} = -\dfrac{7}{6}$

$\therefore$ Gradient of perpendicular line to PQ $= \dfrac{6}{7}$

Equation of line is $y - y_1 = m(x - x_1)$

$y - 0 = \dfrac{6}{7}(x - 3)$

$7y = 6x - 18$

So the line has equation $6x - 7y - 18 = 0$

Whenever you need to find the equation of a straight line your first thought should be: "I need a point, I need a gradient."

I prefer to use this formula when finding the equation of the line because all the numbers are substituted in one go.

It's unlikely you will get an exam question purely on the equations of straight lines. But you will need to use what you know to find, for example, the equation of the tangent or the normal to the point on a given curve.

See examples in the calculus chapter from page 94 onwards.

2.4 Reciprocal Functions

In the reciprocal function $f(x) = \frac{a}{x}$, where a is a constant, the function **decreases** as the x values increase. Specifically, if an x value is multiplied by any number, the y value will be divided by the same number.

Example: The time taken to fly a fixed distance against the speed. (If the speed doubles, the time halves).

Graph: The diagram shows the graphs of two reciprocal functions. They have similar shapes. Each graph is in two sections, with the y-axis being a vertical asymptote. Since they are also self-reflections about $y = x$ this means that a reciprocal function is its own inverse.

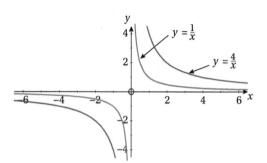

For example, $f(x) = \frac{12}{x} \Rightarrow f^{-1}(x) = \frac{12}{x}$. This is easily seen if 2 is put into the function: $\frac{12}{2} = 6$ then $\frac{12}{6} = 2$.

Reciprocal functions will often be found in transformation questions. For example, if the graph of $f(x) = \frac{1}{x}$ is reflected in the x-axis and then translated along the vector $\begin{pmatrix} 0 \\ -2 \end{pmatrix}$, it will be transformed into the graph of $g(x) = -\frac{1}{x} - 2$. The horizontal asymptote becomes $y = -2$, but the vertical asymptote remains $x = 0$.

And here's an example of a reciprocal function used in a composite function question:

Example: Given that $f(x) = 1 - x$ and $g(x) = \frac{1}{x}, x \neq 0$, find $h(x) = (f \circ g \circ f)(x)$.

Solution: If you put $f(x)$ into $g(x)$ you get $\frac{1}{1-x}$. Now put the new function into f (which in words is "take away from 1") and $(f \circ g \circ f)(x) = 1 - \frac{1}{1-x}, x \neq 1$.

> Now show that $h(x) = \frac{x}{x-1}$. Also find $h^{-1}(x)$ What do you notice? See website for the full working.

Rational functions: Rational functions are defined as functions which themselves have polynomial functions on both the numerator and denominator. In the SL course, study of rational functions is restricted to those of the form $f(x) = \frac{ax+b}{cx+d}$. Since there will always be a value of x which makes the bottom line equal to 0, there will always be a vertical asymptote on the graph of the function at $x = -\frac{d}{c}$. And since the values of b and d become insignificant as x approaches $\pm\infty$, there will always be a horizontal asymptote where $y = \frac{a}{c}$.

When sketching graphs of rational functions, you will be expected to show all asymptotes and axis intercepts.

> Remember that when considering the graph of a function you can replace $f(x)$ with y.

Example: Sketch the graph of the function $f(x) = \frac{2x-3}{x+1}, x \neq -1$

Solution: First, let's work out the x and y intercepts:

- When $x = 0$, $y = -\frac{3}{1} = -3$

- When $y = 0$, $0 = \frac{2x-3}{x+1} \Rightarrow x = 1.5$ (since only the top line will be 0)

Now the asymptotes:

- Looking at the bottom line we see that $x \neq -1$ so $x = -1$ is the vertical asymptote.
- And when x takes on very large values, we can ignore the effect of the -3 and the 1, so $f(x)$ approaches $\frac{2x}{x} = 2$. Thus $y = 2$ is the horizontal asymptote.

Let's put all that information on a sketch.

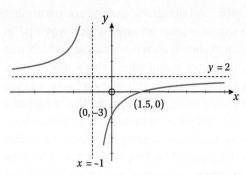

You can now deal with all rational functions in the same way. Note that it is possible for the top line to be a constant, for example $f(x) = \frac{6}{x-3}$. In this case, there is no x intercept (since the function cannot equal zero); and the y intercept is -2. The vertical asymptote is $x = 3$; and the horizontal asymptote is $y = 0$ since the larger value x takes, the smaller the function becomes overall.

Try sketching the following functions and then checking each result by drawing the graph on your GDC. In the last example, you will have to rewrite the equation as a rational function, or you could transform the graph of $y = \frac{2}{x-1}$.

(a) $f(x) = \frac{2x+3}{2x-4}$; (b) $f(x) = \frac{2}{x+1}$; (c) $f(x) = \frac{5-2x}{x}$; (d) $f(x) = 4 + \frac{2}{x-1}$

Questions may involve functions where constants are given as letters instead of numbers. You can be pretty certain that at some stage you will be asked to find their values, often by substituting the coordinates of a point.

Let $f(x) = \dfrac{qx}{2x-p}$

(a) The graph of f has a vertical asymptote $x = 4$. Find the value of p.

(b) The point $(5, 10)$ lies on the graph of f. Find the value of q.

(c) Write down the equation of the horizontal asymptote to the graph of f.

(a) $2x - p = 0$ $\quad$ $8 - p = 0$ $\quad$ $p = 8$ (b) $y = \dfrac{qx}{2x-8}$ Substitute $(5, 10)$ to get $10 = \dfrac{5q}{2}$ So $q = 4$ (c) $f(x) = \dfrac{4x}{2x-8}$ Horizontal asymptote is $y = 2$	*a) For the vertical asymptote, put the bottom line equal to 0.* *b) When you find values of constants, always rewrite the function containing the new information.* *c) Again, now we know the values of p and q, we can write down the function. To find the horizontal asymptote we are interested in very large values of x, so can ignore the 8.*

2.5 Quadratic Functions

Quadratic functions occur in many different situations. You should be completely familiar with the connections between the functions and their graphs, and with the methods for solving quadratic equations.

Equation: $f(x) = ax^2 + bx + c$

Graph: All quadratic graphs are parabolas, the sign of a determining "which way up." In the form shown above, we can say which way up the graph is and where the y-intercept is. For example, the graph of $y = x^2 + 3x - 4$ cuts the y-axis at $(0, -4)$ and is in the shape of a U. The graph is always symmetrical about the vertical line passing through the vertex (turning point), a fact which can often be used when answering questions about the graph. The equation of this line is $x = -\dfrac{b}{2a}$.

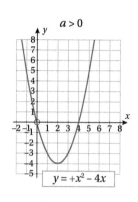

$a > 0$

$y = +x^2 - 4x$

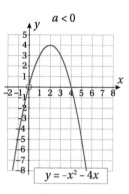

$a < 0$

$y = -x^2 - 4x$

Factorisation: Not all quadratic expressions factorise. For those that do, the method you use depends on whether b or c equals 0.

If $c = 0$, simply take the common factor out.

$$2x^2 - 6x = 2x(x - 3)$$

> Expressions of the form $x^2 + a^2$ *do not factorise.*

If $b = 0$, you can only factorise if the quadratic is of the form $x^2 - a^2$.

$$x^2 - 25 = (x + 5)(x - 5)$$

If all three terms are present, the quadratic will factorise if you can find two numbers which add to give b and multiply to give c.

$$x^2 + 3x - 10 = (x + 5)(x - 2) \textbf{ because } 5 + (-2) = 3 \text{ and } 5 \times 2 = 10$$

Don't forget to look for a common factor first

$$3x^2 + 21x + 36 = 3(x^2 + 7x + 12) = 3(x + 4)(x + 3)$$

$$2x^2 - 32 = 2(x^2 - 16) = 2(x + 4)(x - 4)$$

In factorised form, the equation reveals the x-intercepts of the graph, also known as the *roots* of the quadratic equation. In the five examples above, the x-intercepts are: $(0,0)$ and $(3, 0)$; $(-5, 0)$ and $(5, 0)$; $(-5, 0)$ and $(2, 0)$; $(-4, 0)$ and $(-3, 0)$; $(-4, 0)$ and $(4, 0)$. If you are given these intercepts you can, of course, work back to the equation.

Completing the square: this method gives a third form of writing a quadratic function. The following shows the method and a corresponding example.

1. For $x^2 + bx + c$ start by writing $(x + d)^2$ where $d = b \div 2$.	$x^2 + 6x + 7$ $(x + 3)^2 \ldots$
2. Now write down $-d^2$	$(x + 3)^2 - 9 \ldots$
3. Write down c and simplify.	$(x + 3)^2 - 9 + 7 = (x + 3)^2 - 2$
For quadratics where $a \neq 1$, start by taking a out as a common factor. Forget about it whilst completing the square. Multiply it back at the end.	$2x^2 - 6x - 4 = 2(x^2 - 3x - 2)$ $\qquad = 2((x - 1.5)^2 - 2.25 - 2)$ $\qquad = 2((x - 1.5)^2 - 4.25)$ $\qquad = 2(x - 1.5)^2 - 8.5$

In this form, the function can be seen to be a transformation of $y = x^2$. In the first example above, the transformation is a translation of $\begin{pmatrix} -3 \\ -2 \end{pmatrix}$. Since the vertex of $y = x^2$ is $(0, 0)$, the vertex of the new quadratic will be $(-3, -2)$. In general, the completed square form is always $f(x) = a(x - h)^2 + k$ and this gives a vertex of (h, k).

> When an exam questions says write in the form $a(x - h)^2 + k$, you are being asked to complete the square.

Example: Express $f(x) = x^2 - 4x + 9$ in the form $f(x) = (x - h)^2 + k$. Hence, or otherwise, write down the coordinates of the vertex of the parabola with equation $y = x^2 - 4x + 9$.

Solution: $f(x) = (x - 2)^2 - 2^2 + 9 = (x - 2)^2 + 5$. The vertex is $(2, 5)$. For the "otherwise", we could have found the x-coordinate of the vertex using differentiation, and then substituted to find the y-coordinate. We could also have found the x-coordinate using the fact that the line of symmetry is given by the formula $x = -\dfrac{b}{2a} = -\dfrac{-4}{2} = 2$.

Let $f(x) = a(x - 3)^2 + 6$.

(a) Write down the coordinates of the vertex of the graph of f.

(b) Given that $f(7) = -18$, find the value of a.

(c) Hence find the y-intercept of the graph of f.

(a) $(3, 6)$	*a) The function is in completed square form, so we can write down the vertex with no further working.*
(b) $-18 = a(7 - 3)^2 + 6$	
$\quad -18 = 16a + 6$	*b) $f(7) = -18$ is exactly the same as saying that when $x = 7$, $y = -18$. Substitute into the equation.*
$\quad\quad a = -1.5$	
(c) So $f(x) = -1.5(x - 3)^2 + 6$	
When $x = 0$, $y = -1.5 \times 9 + 6 = -7.5$	*c) The y-intercept is found by putting $x = 0$. But first, having found a, write out the equation.*
y-intercept is $(0, -7.5)$	

2.6 Solving Quadratic Equations

Except for the simplest form of quadratic equation shown on the right the first move is *always collect together terms on the left with 0 on the right*.

> $x^2 = 25$
> $x = \pm 5$

Factorisation: If the quadratic expression factorises, this is the simplest method of solution. Make sure you understand the connection between the factors and the x-intercepts (see previous section) since questions can link the equation to the graph.

> Example: $2x^2 - 4x = x^2 - 3$
> $x^2 - 4x + 3 = 0$
> $(x - 3)(x - 1) = 0$
> $x = 3$ or 1

Formula: *All* quadratic equations (if they have solutions) can be solved using the formula, although it is most useful when the expression does not factorise. The solution of $ax^2 + bx + c = 0$ is: $x = \dfrac{-b \pm \sqrt{b^2 - 4ac}}{2a}$. It is the $\pm$ which leads to the two possible solutions. Your GDC will also have a quadratic equation solver you can use.

Be careful to substitute correctly, particularly when there are minus signs around. Follow the second example in the notes box carefully.

> Example: $2x^2 - 4x = x + 2$
> $2x^2 - 5x - 2 = 0$
> $x = \dfrac{-(-5) \pm \sqrt{(-5)^2 - 4 \times 2 \times (-2)}}{2 \times 2}$
> $x = \dfrac{5 \pm \sqrt{41}}{4}$
> $\therefore x = 2.851$ or -0.351

The graph of $f(x) = x^2 + cx + d$ has a line of symmetry $x = -2.5$. The distance between the two zeros (roots) is 7. Find the value of the two zeros, and hence the values of c and d.	
The two zeros are equidistant from the line of symmetry, so will be at 3.5 either side of –2.5. So the zeros are at $x = 1$ and $x = -6$. The quadratic is $f(x) = (x - 1)(x + 6)$ $\qquad = x^2 + 5x - 6$ and so $c = 5$, $d = -6$.	*The important thing to understand in this question is the connection between the algebra and the geometry. A question could work from factors to roots to line of symmetry/ turning point; this one does all of that in reverse.*

Discriminant: The solutions of a quadratic equation are the points where the graph of the quadratic crosses the x-axis: the diagrams show that this could mean 0, 1 or 2 solutions. In the formula, if the value of $b^2 - 4ac < 0$, we would be trying the find the square root of a negative number – not possible, so no solutions. If the value = 0 there will be 1 solution, and if it's > 0, there are two solutions. Because it discriminates between the number of solutions, $b^2 - 4ac$ is known as the discriminant, and can be represented by the symbol Δ (Greek delta). So any question which asks you about the number of solutions of a quadratic equation will in fact be about the discriminant.

Questions may use the wording "two distinct roots" for 2 solutions, "two equal roots" for 1 solution.

One point to note: when there is one solution, it is often called a "repeated root" or "two equal roots." This is because it always arises from an equation such as $(x - 4)^2 = 0$, the solution $x = 4$ effectively being repeated.

This example shows the typical use of the discriminant in a question.

Example: Let $f(x) = 4x^2 - 12x + k$. Find k if the equation $f(x) = 0$ has two equal roots.

Solution: $\Delta = (-12)^2 - 4 \times 4 \times k = 144 - 16k$. For two equal roots $\Delta = 0$, so $144 - 16k = 0$, giving $k = 9$. Note: $4x^2 - 12x + 9 = (2x - 3)^2$ $\rightarrow$ the repeated root is $x = 1.5$

Find the possible values of k such that the graphs of $y = x^2 + k$ and $y = kx - 3$ have two intersections.	
Graphs intersect when $x^2 + k = kx - 3$ $\qquad x^2 - kx + (k + 3) = 0$ $\qquad \Delta = (-k)^2 - 4(k + 3) = k^2 - 4k - 12$ Two solutions when $\Delta > 0$, so: $\qquad k^2 - 4k - 12 > 0$ $\qquad (k - 6)(k + 2) > 0$ $\qquad k < -2$ or $k > 6$	*To find the points where two graphs intersect, put the two equations equal to each other. We then see that we have a quadratic equation, so write it in the form $ax^2 + bx + c = 0$.* *Now we aren't asked to find the points, but the values of k which give us two solutions – hence the need to find the discriminant. This leads to a quadratic inequality – make sure you know how to solve these.*

Answers

1. (a) –3, 5; (b) 1, 4;
(c) –1.5; 4, (d) –1, –7

2. (a) Min (2, –2);
(b) Min (1, 4);
(c) Max (1.5, 7.25)

3. (a) –2.22, 0.225;
(b) –1.37, 0.366

4. $p < -1$ or $p > 1$

5. $2x^2 - x - 66 = 0$,
6 cm × 4 cm

6. $k = 20$, (2.5, 0), (2, 1) and
(3, 1)

7. $a = 2$, $x = 2$, (2, 8)

Quadratics: Practice Exercise

Quadratics are extremely important in this course. Many algebraic situations tend to resolve to a quadratic equation, and you could be expected to use any of the methods above to solve them. It is inevitable that you will find a number of questions involving quadratics in both papers, so here's the chance for some practice in the various techniques you will need.

1. Solve these quadratics using factorisation, rearranging into the form $ax^2 + bx + c = 0$ as necessary:

   (a) $x^2 - x + 2 = x + 17$

   (b) $x = 5 - \dfrac{4}{x}$

   (c) $2x^2 - 5x - 12 = 0$

   (d) $20x^2 + 160x + 140 = 0$

2. Write each of the following in the form $a(x - h)^2 + k$, and state the turning point on the associated graph, and whether it is a maximum or minimum:

   (a) $x^2 - 4x + 6$

   (b) $2x^2 - 4x + 6$

   (c) $5 + 3x - x^2$

3. Use the formula to solve the following equations to 3SF:

   (a) $2x^2 + 4x - 1 = 0$

   (b) $(x - 1)^2 = 6 - (x + 2)^2$

4. The equation $x^2 - 2px + 1 = 0$ has two distinct roots. Find the set of possible values of p.

5. The area of the shape on the right is $33\,\text{cm}^2$.

   Set up an equation in x and solve to find the dimensions of the rectangle.

   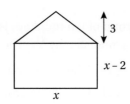

6. The function $f(x) = 4x^2 - kx + 25$ where $k > 0$ has its vertex on the x-axis. Find the value of k, the coordinates of the vertex, and the point of intersection of the graph of f with the line $y = 1$.

7. The graph shows the function $f(x) = 8x - ax^2$. The x-intercepts are at $(0, 0)$ and $(4, 0)$. Find the value of a, the equation of the line of symmetry, and the coordinates of the vertex.

   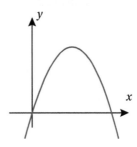

2.7 Exponential and Logarithmic Functions

Equations: $f(x) = a^x$ where $a > 0$

                 $f(x) = \log_a x$ where $x > 0$

Notice the domains. Remember, it is not possible to take the log of a negative number.

Graphs: In the same way that all quadratics have the same shape, graphs of $y = a^x$ have the same shape for different values of a, and all pass through (0, 1). Since $\log_a x$ is the inverse of a^x their graphs are reflections of each other in the line $y = x$, and the graph of $y = \log_a x$ passes through (1, 0) for all a.

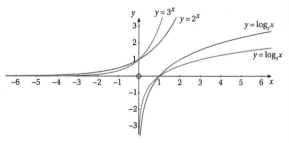

Questions draw on your knowledge of the laws of indices and logarithms. You must be familiar with the following rules:

- If $a^x = b$ then $x = \log_a b$ (eg: $2^3 = 8$, so $\log_2 8 = 3$)
- $x = \log_a a^x$ This is similar to $x = \sqrt{x^2}$
- $x = a^{\log_a x}$ This is similar to $x = (\sqrt{x})^2$

e^x and $\ln x$: The number e is, like π, given a letter because it is irrational and hence impossible to write accurately using decimals. It is approximately 2.718. The functions e^x and e^{-x} are important because they are used to model situations where the rate of growth or decay of the quantity x is dependent on the value of x at any time. Typical applications are population growth and radioactive decay. The inverse of e^x is $\ln x$, short for $\log_e x$.

> Using the rules in the previous paragraph, remember that $e^{\ln x}$ and $\ln e^x$ both simplify to x. For example, $e^{2\ln x} = e^{\ln x^2} = x^2$

A group of ten monkeys is introduced to a zoo. After t years the number of monkeys, N, is modelled by $N = 10e^{0.3t}$.

(a) How many monkeys are there after 3 years?

(b) How many complete months will it take for the number of monkeys to reach 50?

(a) $N = 10\,e^{0.3 \times 3} = 24.596...$ ∴ There are 24 monkeys (b) $50 = 10\,e^{0.3t}$ $5 = e^{0.3t}$ $\ln 5 = \ln e^{0.3t}$ $\ln 5 = 0.3t$ $t = 5.36...$ years $= 64.38$ months ∴ There will be 50 monkeys after 65 months	*An important point to note in the answers to this question is that they are not rounded in the normal way. In part (a) there are only 24.596 monkeys after three years, so the 25th monkey hasn't appeared yet! The answer would still be 24 even if the calculation came to 24.99.* *And in part (b), although 64.38 rounds to give 64, there won't be 50 monkeys after 64 months. In terms of complete months, the answer is 65.*

You will find plenty more practice with logarithmic and exponential functions in the Calculus chapter starting on page 86.

Functions: Long Answer Questions

The answers to these Section B style questions are given below each, but full working may be found online.

1. Let $f(x) = 2x - 4$ and $g(x) = \dfrac{3}{2x}$, for $x \neq 0$.

   (a) Find $f^{-1}(x)$

   $h(x) = (g \circ f^{-1})(x)$

   (b) Show that $h(x) = \dfrac{3}{x+4}$ stating the domain

   The graph of h has a horizontal asymptote at $y = 0$

   (c) (i) Find the y-intercept of the graph of h

       (ii) Sketch the graph of h, $-6 \leq x \leq 6$, showing any axis intercepts and asymptotes

   (d) For the graph of h^{-1},

       (i) Write down the x-intercept

       (ii) Write down the equation of the vertical asymptote

   (e) Given that $h^{-1}(a) = -1$, find the value of a.

___

Answers:

(a) $f^{-1}(x) = \dfrac{x+4}{2}$

(c) (i) $y = 0.75$ (ii)
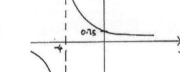

(d) (i) $x = 0.75$ (ii) $x = 0$

(e) $a = 1$

2. Let $f(x) = a\log_2 x$

   (a) Given that $f^{-1}\left(-\tfrac{2}{3}\right) = \tfrac{1}{4}$, find the value of a

   (b) Write down $f^{-1}(0)$

   (c) Show that $f^{-1}(x) = 2^{3x}$

   Function g is obtained by translating f^{-1} +1 unit parallel to the x-axis.

   (d) Show that $g(x) = \dfrac{1}{k} \times f^{-1}(x)$ where k is an integer to be evaluated.

___

Answers:

(a) $a = \dfrac{1}{3}$

(b) 1

(d) $k = 8$

3. The diagram shows part of the graph of $f(x) = bx^2 - (10 - b)x + c$. The y-intercept is at $(0, 6)$. The x-intercepts are at P and Q.

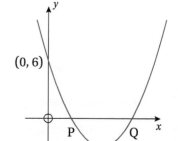

(a) Write down the value of c.

(b) Given that P $= (1, 0)$, show that $b = 2$.

(c) Write $f(x)$ in the form $a(x - h)^2 + k$ where a, h and k are integers to be found.

(d) Use your answer to part (c) to write down:

    (i) The equation of the line of symmetry of the graph.

    (ii) The coordinates of the vertex of the graph.

(e) Write $f(x)$ in the form $p(x - q)(x - r)$ and hence or otherwise find the coordinates of Q.

Answers:

(a) $c = 6$

(c) $f(x) = 2(x - 2)^2 - 2$, $a = 2$, $h = 2$, $k = -2$

(d) (i) $x = 2$ (ii) $(2, -2)$

(e) $f(x) = 2(x - 1)(x - 3)$, Q $= (3, 0)$

4. Given the function $p(x) = e^{x-4} - 3$

(a) The function $p(x)$ has been translated along the vector $\binom{r}{t}$, to the function $f(x) = e^{x-1} + 2$. Write down the values of r and t.

(b) Show that $f^{-1}(x) = \ln(x - 2) + 1$, $x > 2$.

(c) Given $g(x) = 1$. The point of intersection between $f^{-1}(x)$ and $g(x)$ is point A. Find the coordinates of point A.

(d) Point B is the x-intercept of $y = e^{-(x+3)} - 1$. Find the x-coordinate of B.

(e) The function $h(x)$ which passes through A and B is shown on the graph below. Find p and q where $h(x) = \log_p(x + q)$.

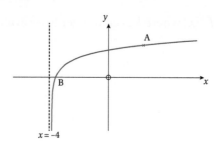

Answers:

(a) $r = -3$, $t = -5$

(c) A $= (3, 1)$

(d) $x = -3$

(e) $p = 7$, $q = 4$

5. Let $f(x) = \dfrac{20x}{e^{0.3x}}$ where $0 \leq x \leq 20$

    (a) Sketch the graph of f.

    (b) Find the x-coordinate of the maximum point.

    (c) State the range of values of x for which f is an increasing function.

    Let $g(x) = \dfrac{20}{x}$ where $0 \leq x \leq 20$.

    (d) Add the graph of g to your sketch.

    (e) Find the x-coordinate of the point of intersection of the graphs of f and g, and explain why this is the solution of the equation $x^2 = e^{0.3x}$.

    (f) Find $f(20)$ and $g(20)$ and hence state whether there is a second solution to the equation.

    _____

Answers:

(b) $x = 3.33$ (a) (d)

(c) $0 \leq x < 3.33$

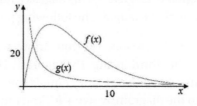

(e) $x = 1.197$. Rearrange $\dfrac{20}{x} = \dfrac{20x}{e^{0.3x}}$

(f) $f(20) = 0.992$, $g(20) = 1$.
     Yes, there is.

Chapter 3: GEOMETRY AND TRIGONOMETRY

3.1 Solution of Triangles

Right-angled triangles: This page is a reminder of how to deal with the sides and angles of a right-angled triangle. The following page deals with non right-angled triangles.

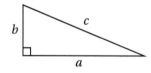

Pythagoras' Theorem: If you know two sides of a right-angled triangle, you can calculate the third using Pythagoras' Theorem. This states that the square of the hypotenuse (the longest side) equals the sum of the squares of the two shorter sides. As applied to the diagram, $c^2 = a^2 + b^2$. You must remember to subtract if you already have the hypotenuse (it's always opposite the right angle) and want to calculate one of the other sides. For example, $b^2 = c^2 - a^2$.

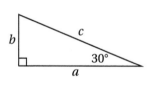

Trigonometry: There is no mystery to sin, cos and tan. They simply represent the ratios of pairs of sides for a triangle with given angles. For example, suppose the smallest angle in the triangle is 30°. Whatever the *size* of the triangle, b turns out to be half of c. The ratio of b to c is called the sine (sin for short), so $\sin 30° = 0.5$. The ratio of a to c is called the cosine (cos), and b to a is the tangent (tan). If you use the following procedure ***in all cases*** then every question can be worked out in the same way, and you should always get the right answer.

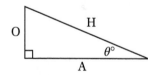

1. Label the three sides of the triangle with H (for hypotenuse, the side opposite the right angle), O (for opposite, the side opposite the angle you are dealing with) and A (for adjacent, the side next to the angle).

2. For the two sides you are dealing with, write down the word sin, cos or tan according to the mnemonic SOH/CAH/TOA.

3. Now write down the angle (which may be unknown) followed by an equals sign.

4. On the right hand side of the equals sign, you will write down a fraction (O over H, A over H or O over A) which will either involve two known sides, or one known and one unknown side.

5. You will now have an equation to solve. The three examples below show how to do this.

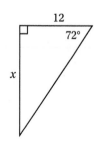

Example 1: Find x.

x is O, 12 is A, so we use tan.

Write down tan, then the angle, then =, then the fraction O/A.

To solve this equation, just multiply through by 12.

$\tan 72° = \dfrac{x}{12}$

$12 \times \tan 72° = x$

$x = 36.9°$

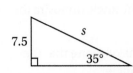

Example 2: Find *s*.

s is H, 7.5 is O, so we use sin.

Write down sin, then the angle, then =, then the fraction O/H.

The unknown is now on the bottom of the fraction, so we must cross-multiply to find *s*.

$$\sin 35° = \frac{7.5}{s}$$

$$s = \frac{7.5}{\sin 35°}$$

$$s = 13.1$$

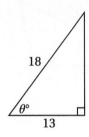

Example 3: Find the angle $\theta°$.

13 is A, 18 is H, so we use cos.

Write down cos, then the angle, then =, then the fraction A/H.

Calculate the value of the fraction, then use the $\cos^{-1}$ function to find out the angle ($\cos^{-1}$ means "find the angle whose cosine is...")

$$\cos \theta = \frac{13}{18}$$

$$\cos \theta = 0.7222$$

$$\theta = \cos^{-1} 0.7222$$

$$\theta = 43.8°$$

Having worked out $\frac{13}{18}$ leave the answer on the display. Then work out the angle using $\cos^{-1}$ANS. This ensures full accuracy.

Sine and Cosine Rules: For triangles which are *not* right-angled we use the sine and cosine rules. The triangle shown has the conventional notation of small letters for the lengths of sides and capital letters for the angles opposite. To find lengths and angles, use:

- The sine rule if 2 sides and 2 angles are involved, unless one of the angles is between the two sides
- The cosine rule if 3 sides and 1 angle are involved

SINE RULE
$$\frac{a}{\sin A} = \frac{b}{\sin B} = \frac{c}{\sin C}$$

COSINE RULE
$c^2 = a^2 + b^2 - 2ab \cos C$ *(for a side)*
$\cos C = \frac{a^2 + b^2 - c^2}{2ab}$ *(for an angle)*

Don't be put off by the letters. Basically, the sine rule says the ratio of side/sine is the same for each pair of sides and angles. And in both versions of the cosine rule, ensure that the side *c* matches the angle *C*.

In triangle ABC, angle B = 43°, AC = 6.8 cm and AB = 4.3 cm. Find the size of angle A giving your answer to the nearest degree.

$$\frac{\sin C}{4.3} = \frac{\sin 43}{6.8}$$

$$\sin C = \frac{4.3 \sin 43}{6.8} = 0.4313$$

$$\therefore C = 25.55°$$

So $A = 180 - (43 + 25.55) = 111.45$

$A = 111°$ to the nearest degree.

It's very useful to draw a quick sketch to see how to proceed.

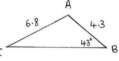

We know 2 sides and 1 angle, and we want another angle, so we use the sine rule (which I've inverted to make the calculation easier – always start by writing the thing you want to work out).

In this case we can only work out C from the sine rule, but then we can use the sum of the angles to find A. Note that you should always work to more figures than you need.

Example: A triangle has sides 4, $\sqrt{48}$ and 8. Calculate the size of the angle opposite the side with length $\sqrt{48}$.

Solution: This time we need the cosine rule in its second form, making sure that the side labelled c in the formula is opposite the required angle.

Make life easy for yourself by remembering that you don't need a calculator to find the square of a square root!

$$\cos C = \frac{4^2 + 8^2 - (\sqrt{48})^2}{2 \times 4 \times 8}.$$ Check that this gives C = 60°.

Ambiguous case using the sine rule: Suppose we are given a triangle where AC = 8, BC = 5, and angle A = 30°. The diagram shows that with this information there are two possible triangles which can be drawn, and hence two possible values for angle B – this is known as the *ambiguous case*. Having found one answer, the other can be found by subtracting from 180°. In this case, B_1 is 126.9° and B_2 is 53.1°.

Note that there won't always be two answers – it depends on the given numbers. The wording of a question should give you a clue.

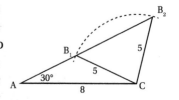

Area of a non-right angled triangle: If you know two sides of a triangle, and the size of the angle between the two sides, then the area of the triangle can be found using: Area $= \frac{1}{2} ab \sin C$.

But don't forget the alternative formula $A = \frac{1}{2} \times$ base $\times$ height which is useful if two sides are perpendicular.

Example: A triangle has sides 5, 7, and 8. Find the size of the smallest angle and the area of the triangle.

Solution: The smallest angle is opposite the shortest side. Using the cosine rule we get $\cos x = \frac{7^2 + 8^2 - 5^2}{2 \times 7 \times 8} = 0.786$.

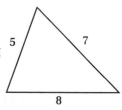

This gives an angle of 38.2°. The sides either side of this angle are 7 and 8, so the area is $\frac{1}{2} \times 7 \times 8 \times \sin 38.2° = 17.3$

Bearings: One of the practical applications of non-right angled trigonometry is the calculation of distances and angles for moving ships and planes. Their direction of travel is based on compass directions, called *bearings*. A bearing is an angle measured around clockwise from North. Always draw in North lines on your diagrams before marking in bearings.

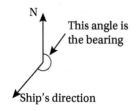

If a question involves bearings between places, check whether you are dealing with the bearing of A *from* B or the bearing from A *to* B, which is the other way round. Use arrows to show in which direction to take the bearing, and put the North line at the *start* of the arrow.

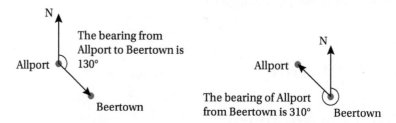

There is always a difference of 180° between bearings in opposite directions.

If you find calculations with bearings a bit confusing, I suggest you work through the following question with me. It's important that you work with a large, clear sketch. Also, at the risk of repeating myself, note that I have worked to 4SF in order to give accurate answers to 3SF.

A ship sails from port P and travels due South to port Q. From port Q it sails on a bearing of 065° and travels for 45 km to a point R, which is due East of P.

(a) (i) Draw and label clearly a diagram to show P, Q and R.

    (ii) Calculate the distance form port P to point R.

In questions like this the diagram is an important tool, so make it large. Angles do not have to be accurate or lengths drawn to scale, but make them look approximately right.

(i)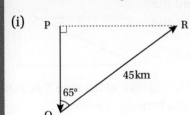

(ii) $\sin 65° = \dfrac{PR}{45} \Rightarrow PR = 45\sin 65° = 40.8$

The distance from P to R is 40.8 km

A second ship also sails from port P for 45 km to a point S, but on a bearing of 330°.

(b) Complete your diagram in part (a) to show point S.

(c) Calculate the distance from R to S (shown with a dotted line) and the angle PRS.

Rather than putting in 330°, the more useful 30° has been shown instead. The 40.8 has also been put in: always keep your diagrams up-to-date with new information.

To calculate RS, we use triangle PRS which is not right angled. We already know two sides and one angle (SPR = 30 + 90 = 120°), so we use the cosine rule:

(b)

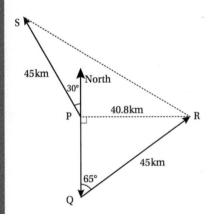

(c)

$RS^2 = 45^2 + 40.783^2 - 2 \times 45 \times 40.783 \times \cos 120°$

$RS = \sqrt{5523.5} = 74.3 \text{ km}$

(Check: RS < RP + PS. Looks OK)

Now we need to calculate angle PRS. We know one angle and two sides so we use the sine rule.

So angle PRS = $\sin^{-1}(0.5244) = 31.6°$

---

d) What is the bearing of S from R?

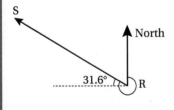

The diagram shows the arrow representing S from R, and a new North line inserted. The required bearing has also been put in. How big is this angle? From North round to West is 270°, and then we need another 31.6.

(d) The bearing of S from R is 270 + 31.6

      ∴ R = 301.6°

Answers

1. $b = 5.32$ cm, $c = 7.20$ cm

2. $p = 4.31$ cm, $Q = 79.9°$

3. 80.3 m, $2.87°$

4. 10.9 km, $059.4°$

5. 14.5 cm

6. $A = 36.9°$, $B = 90°$, $C = 53.1°$

7. 9.64 cm

Solution of Triangles: Practice Exercise

1. Triangle ABC has A = 66°, B = 44°, a = 7cm. Find b and c.

2. Triangle PQR has P = 45°, r = 5cm and q = 6cm. Find p and Q.

3. a) An observer on a ship which is 2.3km from the coast measures the angle of elevation of a cliff as 2°. Find the height of the cliff in metres.

   b) A 35 m tower stands on the top of the cliff. Find the angle of depression for an observer looking at the ship from the top of the tower.

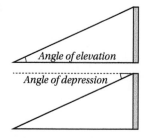
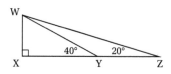

4. A ship S is 7 km away from a lighthouse L on a bearing of 080° and a ship T is 5 km away from L on a bearing of 210°. Find the distance and bearing of S from T.

5. A rhombus has sides of length 8 cm and angles of 50° and 130°. Find the length of the longer diagonal of the rhombus.

6. A triangle ABC has area 24 cm² and sides a = 6 cm, b = 10 cm. Find all the angles in the triangle.

7. Calculate WX, given YZ = 15 cm.

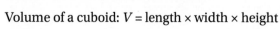

3.2 3-D Geometry

You have to be able to combine the rules of 3-D coordinates with the trigonometry of both right angled and non-right angled triangles in order to find the sides and angles of cuboids, prisms and pyramids.

Cuboid: A cuboid is the 3-D equivalent of a rectangle. It has 12 edges, 4 each in three different dimensions (length, width and height). Commonly asked questions involve the lengths of diagonals (both of sides and also from one corner to the opposite corner) and angles between various lines. The points used will be the vertices (corners) and the midpoints of sides.

Volume of a cuboid: V = length × width × height

Pyramid: You only have to concern yourself with a "right" pyramid as illustrated – ie where the apex is directly above the centre of the base, which is itself a square. Pyramid questions almost invariably use the midpoints of sides, and it should be noted that a line drawn from the midpoint of one of the base edges to the apex is at a right angle to the base edge.

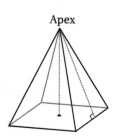

Volume of a pyramid: $V = \frac{1}{3} \times$ base area × height

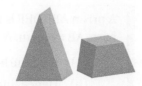

Prism: A prism is any 3-D shape with the same cross-section throughout its length. Very often this cross-section is a triangle, but it does not have to be.

Volume of a prism: V = area of cross section × length

Angle between a line and a plane: A plane is a flat surface, so each of the faces of the 3-D shapes illustrated is a plane.

The angle between a line and a plane is the angle between the line and its *projection* on the plane: think of the projection as part of a "shadow line" on the plane.

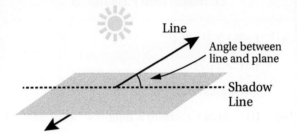

Calculating lengths and angles in 3 dimensions: In every case, you convert the question into an appropriate 2-D question, usually by identifying a right-angled triangle containing the length/angle you have to work out, drawing it as it really looks, then using trigonometry and Pythagoras as usual.

For example, the base edges of a pyramid are 10 cm and the slant edges are 12 cm. M is the midpoint of side PQ and X is the centre point of the base. Find length AM and angle AMX to the nearest degree.

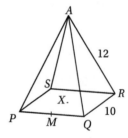

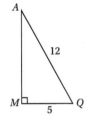

We can find AM using triangle AMQ.

MQ = 5 (half of the base length)

So $AM^2 = 12^2 - 5^2 \Rightarrow AM = \sqrt{119}$.

No need to calculate $\sqrt{119}$ since we are using it in the next stage.

Now we can draw triangle AMX because we know MX = 5 and $AM = \sqrt{119}$.

We can see from the diagram that $\cos M = \dfrac{5}{\sqrt{119}}$ giving M = 62.7°, or 63° to the nearest degree.

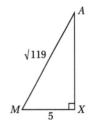

A prism ABCDEF is formed with an isosceles triangle cross section and a rectangular base. AE = 6.4 cm, AB = 5 cm, BC = 11 cm. M is the midpoint of AB.

(a) Find the length of EM.

(b) Hence find

    (i)   The area of triangle AEB

    (ii) The volume of the prism

(c) Find the length of MC, and hence the angle EC makes with base ABCD.

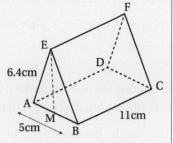

a) $EM^2 + 2.5^2 = 6.4^2$
 	
      $EM^2 = 34.71$
 	
      $EM = 5.89$ cm
 	
 b) (i)   Area $= \frac{1}{2} \times$ base $\times$ height $= \frac{1}{2} \times 5 \times 5.89 = 14.7$ cm²
 	
     (ii) Volume $= 14.7 \times 11 = 162$ cm³
	a) Wherever possible, try to find right-angled triangles which will lead to the solution. In this case we can use EAM, knowing that AM is one half of AB.
	
	 b) Use standard formula for the area of a triangle and the volume of a prism.

c) $MC^2 = 2.5^2 + 11^2$
 	
      $MC = 11.3$ cm 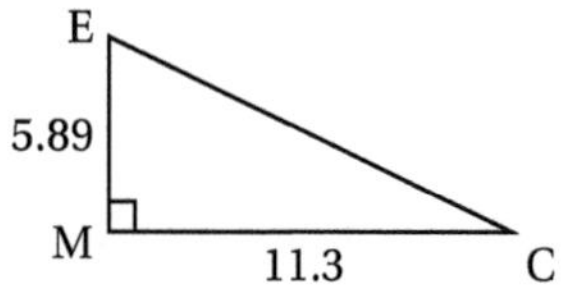
 	
      $\text{Tan(ECM)} = \frac{5.89}{11.3}$
 	
      Angle EC makes with base is 27.6°
	c) Once again we find in EMC a right-angled triangle which will give us MC. It also gives us the angle EC makes with the base.
	
	 As before, I have given answers to 3SF, but worked to 4SF.

(diagram in cell c): triangle with E at top-left, vertical side 5.89, M at bottom-left right angle, base 11.3 to C at bottom-right.

3.3 Cylinder, Sphere and Cone

Curved Surface Area: Whilst the concept of the *volume* of shapes with curved edges and faces may not be too difficult to appreciate, the *area* of such curved faces may be problematic. The way to think of such faces is to imagine them to be made from separate pieces of paper; the area of a curved surface is the same as the area of the paper it is made from when it is flattened out.

For example, unroll the curved surface of a cylinder and you get a rectangle whose height is the height of the cylinder and whose length is the circumference of the cylinder.

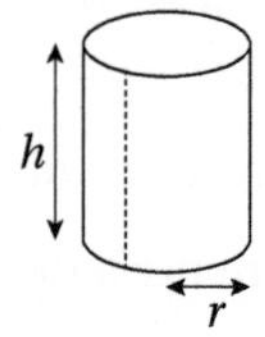

Cut along the dotted line and open up to get...

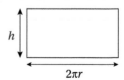

You need to be able to use the relevant area and volume formulae for cylinders, cones and spheres. You will find them all in your list of formulae. They are:

Cylinder: Curved surface area = $2\pi rh$

Volume = $\pi r^2 h$

Cone: Curved surface area = πrl (l is the slant height)

Volume = $\frac{1}{3}\pi r^2 h$

Sphere: Surface area = $4\pi r^2$

Volume = $\frac{4}{3}\pi r^3$

Read each question very carefully to see *exactly* what you are being asked to find. For example, a cylinder may be completely closed in which case the total surface area is the curved surface area plus the areas of the two ends, which are both circles. Or it may be open at one end, so just add one circle.

The volume of a hemisphere is half that of a sphere, but its total surface area will be half the curved surface of a sphere plus the circle which forms its base. Its formula will be $\frac{1}{2} \times 4\pi r^2 + \pi r^2 = 3\pi r^2$.

Example: Both a cone and a hemisphere have base diameter of 18 cm. If the height of the cone is 10 cm, show that the ratio of the volume of the cone to that of the hemisphere is 5:9.

Solution: The volume of the cone is $\frac{1}{3}\pi r^2 h = \frac{1}{3}\pi \times 9^2 \times 10 = 270\pi$. The volume of the hemisphere is $\frac{1}{2} \times \frac{4}{3}\pi r^3 = \frac{2}{3}\pi \times 9^3 = 486\pi$. We may as well leave π in the answers since we are finding the ratio.

So, volume of cone:volume of hemisphere = $270\pi:486\pi = 5:9$

> There's an old trap in this question – all the formulae use the radius, but we have been given the diameter.

Try the following example for yourself.

Example: In the South of England, special brick constructions called "Oast Houses" were built to dry the hops used in making beer. The diagram models an Oast House as a cone on top of a cylinder. Both have base diameter 8 m; the cylinder has a height of 6 m, and the building is 17.4 m high overall.

Find the total surface area of the exposed faces of the Oast House, and the total volume.

You will need the slant height of the cone to find the curved surface area – use Pythagoras' Theorem. Note too that the base of the cone will not form part of the total surface area since it is not an external surface.

Answers: Area = 303 m², Volume = 493 m³.

> Full working can be found on the website

A cylindrical tube of length 40 cm and radius 3.2 cm contains 6 tennis balls each with a radius of 3.14 cm.

(a) Giving answers to 3SF, find

(i) The volume of the tube

(ii) The volume of one tennis ball

(b) Hence find the volume of empty space in the tube.

(a) (i) $V = \pi r^2 l = \pi \times 3.2^2 \times 40 = 1286.7...$ Volume of tube = 1290 cm³ (ii) $V = \frac{4}{3}\pi r^3 = \frac{4}{3}\pi \times 3.14^3 = 129.68...$ Volume of ball = 130 cm³ (b) Volume of 6 tennis balls = 129.68 × 6 $\qquad$ = 778.1 cm³ $\qquad$ Empty space = 1286.7 − 778.1 = 508.6... $\qquad$ = 509 cm³ to 3SF	*If you're going to use a formula, write it down. This shows the examiner what you are using, and helps you to substitute values correctly.* *This question is yet another good example of the importance of working to a higher accuracy than the required answer. If the first two rounded answers were used to obtain the final answer, the result would have been* *1290 − 6 × 130 = 510.*

Geometry: Practice Exercise

Answers

1. 5.44km, 272.2°

2. 10 cm, 13 cm, 67.4°, 12.4 cm, 76.0°, 5 cm, 40.6°

3. Volume of cone = 25.1 cm³

Volume of each sphere = 0.524 cm³

47 spheres, with a bit left over!

1. Three boats P, Q and R are at anchor in a bay. The bearing of P from R is 046°, and of Q from P is 125°. The distance of R from P is 3 km, and of P from Q is 4 km.

(a) Draw a clear diagram showing all the information.

(b) Calculate:

(i) the distance of R from Q;

(ii) the bearing of R from Q.

2. The diagram shows a right pyramid with:

PQ = 8 cm, QR = 6 cm, VW = 12 cm.

W is at the centre of the base, M and N are the midpoints of PQ and QR. Calculate:

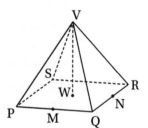

(a) PR

(b) PV

(c) Angle VPW

(d) VM

(e) The angle VM makes with the base

(f) MN

(g) Angle MSN *(Draw triangle MSN first)*

3. A solid cone of height 6 cm and radius 2 cm is melted down to be made into small spheres. If each sphere has a radius of 0.5 cm, how many can be made?

3.4 Circular Functions

Radians: Radians are an alternative to degrees when measuring the size of angles. Although it is easier to **_think_** in degrees, radians are often used with trigonometric functions and **_must_** be used when differentiating or integrating them.

■ *Before* making a start on any trigonometric question, check your calculator is in the right mode.

The conversion is π radians = 180°. (An angle is assumed to be in radians unless the degrees symbol is given).

It is worth memorising some key angles in radians (see table in the notes box). π appears in many angles when expressed in radians (because of the conversion) but it does not have to. For example, 45° = 0.785 radians, but this is not an **_exact_** conversion, unlike $\frac{\pi}{4}$.

$30° = \pi/6$
$45° = \pi/4$
$60° = \pi/3$
$90° = \pi/2$
$120° = 2\pi/3$
$180° = \pi$
$270° = 3\pi/2$
$360° = 2\pi$

There are two circle formulae which are used when a sector angle is expressed in radians. If the angle is θ and the radius of the circle is r:

- Arc length of sector = $r\theta$
- Area of sector = $\frac{1}{2}r^2\theta$

The diagram shows two concentric circles with radii 1 and 4. The area S is enclosed by arcs AB and CD, and lines AD and BC. Given that angle AOB = $\frac{\pi}{3}$, find:

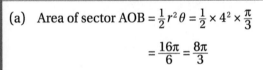

a) The area of S

b) The perimeter of S

simplifying your answers and giving them in an exact form.

(a)   Area of sector AOB = $\frac{1}{2}r^2\theta = \frac{1}{2} \times 4^2 \times \frac{\pi}{3}$

$$= \frac{16\pi}{6} = \frac{8\pi}{3}$$

Area of sector DOC = $\frac{1}{2} \times 1^2 \times \frac{\pi}{3}$

$$= \frac{\pi}{6}$$

Area of S = Area AOB – Area DOC

$$= \frac{8\pi}{3} - \frac{\pi}{6} = \frac{15\pi}{6}$$

(b)   Perimeter of S = AD +BC + arc AB + arc DC

$$= 3 + 3 + \frac{4\pi}{3} + \frac{\pi}{3}$$

$$= 6 + \frac{5\pi}{3}$$

Often an odd shaped area is found by subtracting two friendly shaped areas!

Notice how I have used words to explain to the examiner what each calculation is about, rather than just an amorphous mass of calculations. And, in case you've done your sums wrong, it's important to state that you're subtracting the two areas, and what you've added to get the perimeter. There are method marks for these, even if all the numbers are wrong!

Trigonometric functions: The diagram shows a circle with radius 1 (a *unit circle*). A line is drawn from the centre to a point on the circumference, and this forms angle θ with the x-axis. The x-coordinate of the point is defined as the cosine of the angle ($\cos\theta$) and the y-coordinate as the sine ($\sin\theta$).

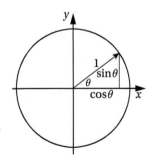

These definitions will apply as the line rotates full circle, giving the sin and cos for all angles from 0° to 360°.

When these are plotted as graphs, we get the following:

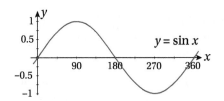

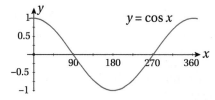

These graphs can, of course, be extended to show the sin and cos for *all* angles.

Points to note:

- The range of both functions is $-1 \leq f(x) \leq 1$
- $\sin x > 0$ for angles between 0° and 180°
- $\cos x > 0$ for angles between 0° and 90°, also between 270° and 360°
- Both functions have a *period* (ie repeat themselves) every 360°.

The graph of $\tan x$ is still *periodic* but with a period of 180° rather than 360°. It also has vertical asymptotes at 90°, 270° and so on.

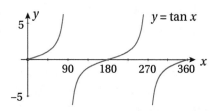

Exact values of sin, cos and tan: Although the trigonometric ratios for most angles have to be calculated using a GDC, some key angles have easily remembered values.

You should learn the following table:

Angle in degrees	0	30	45	60	90
Angle in radians	0	$\dfrac{\pi}{6}$	$\dfrac{\pi}{4}$	$\dfrac{\pi}{3}$	$\dfrac{\pi}{2}$
sin	0	$\dfrac{1}{2}$	$\dfrac{\sqrt{2}}{2}$	$\dfrac{\sqrt{3}}{2}$	1
cos	1	$\dfrac{\sqrt{3}}{2}$	$\dfrac{\sqrt{2}}{2}$	$\dfrac{1}{2}$	0
tan	0	$\dfrac{1}{\sqrt{3}}$	1	$\sqrt{3}$	∞

remember

A neat way to remember the exact values for sin (ie the third row of the table) is that they form the series $\dfrac{\sqrt{0}}{2}, \dfrac{\sqrt{1}}{2}, \dfrac{\sqrt{2}}{2}, \dfrac{\sqrt{3}}{2}, \dfrac{\sqrt{4}}{2}$.

Also note that $\dfrac{\sqrt{2}}{2} = \dfrac{1}{\sqrt{2}}$; choose whichever form is more convenient in a particular question.

You can now use this table, combined with the symmetries of the graphs, to calculate trigonometric ratios for angles greater than 90°. So, if I needed to find the value of $\sin 210°$ I would note from the graph that it is the same as $\sin 30°$ but with a negative sign. Thus, $\sin 210° = -\dfrac{1}{2}$.

Try the following, and check your answers on your GDC:

$$\cos 135°; \ \sin \dfrac{3\pi}{4}; \ \sin 180°; \ \tan \dfrac{4\pi}{3}; \ \tan 225°; \ \cos \dfrac{11\pi}{6}.$$

Instead of using graph symmetries, you may have been shown how to use unit circles to deal with angles greater than 90°. See the website for a full explanation.

Calculate the side BC of a triangle where AB = 4 cm, AC = 3 cm and angle A = 120°.	

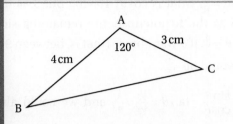

A sketch is always useful, even in a relatively simple question such as this one – it ensures you use the formula correctly.

$BC^2 = 4^2 + 3^2 - 2 \times 4 \times 3 \cos 120°$

$BC^2 = 16 + 9 - 24 \times (-0.5)$

$BC^2 = 25 + 12$

$BC = \sqrt{37}$ cm

This is a non-calculator question, so we have to be able to work out cos 120° without the help of a GDC.

Note that I haven't cut any corners with the working, and I've put the negative number in a bracket. It all helps to ensure correct arithmetic.

BC is just over 6 cm – check it looks about right.

3.5 Trigonometric equations

What is the value of θ given $\sin\theta = 0.5$, $0° \leq \theta \leq 360°$? We want to know what angle has a sin which is 0.5, and this is 30°; then, using the symmetry of the sin graph, we can see that 150° is also a solution. (If the domain is in radians, you can either work in degrees and convert at the end, or set your calculator to radians: this gives $\theta = \frac{\pi}{6}$ or $\frac{5\pi}{6}$. On paper 2, a simple way to solve the equation is to find the intersections of $y = \sin x$ and $y = 0.5$ within the given domain.

Example: Solve $\cos(\theta - 30) = \frac{\sqrt{2}}{2}$, where $-180° \leq \theta \leq 180°$.

Solution: $\arccos\left(\frac{\sqrt{2}}{2}\right) = 45°$ or $-45°$. This gives values of $\theta - 30$, so
$\theta = 45 + 30$ or $-45 + 30 = 75°$ or $-15°$.

The example above shows how important it is to take note of the domain when solving trigonometric equations - the domain will also let you know whether the answer should be in degrees or radians. Try the following simple equations (GDC for numbers 1 and 2).

Answers:

1. $\sin x = -0.783$, $0° \leq x \leq 360°$ 1. 231.5°, 308.5°

2. $\tan x = 1.5$, $0 \leq x \leq 2\pi$ 2. 0.983, 4.12

3. $2\tan x = 2$, $0 \leq x \leq \pi$ 3. $\frac{\pi}{4}$

4. $\sin(x - 60) = \frac{1}{2}$, $0° \leq x \leq 360°$ 4. 90°, 330°

When solving using arctan, solutions simply repeat every 180°. It's not necessary to use graph symmetry or unit circle.

Trigonometric identities: The identities in the notes box should be memorised, although they are all in the formula book. We shall use them in the following sections.

With these identities we can solve equations such as $3\sin^2 x = \cos^2 x$ and $\sin 2x = \sin x$. In the first case we can replace $\cos^2 x$ by $1 - \sin^2 x$ thus creating the equation $\sin^2 x = \frac{1}{4}$. Alternatively, divide both sides by $\cos^2 x$ to get $\tan^2 x = \frac{1}{3}$. In the second case, replace $\sin 2x$ by $2\sin x \cos x$ and rearrange to get $\sin x(2\cos x - 1) = 0$.

$\tan\theta \equiv \dfrac{\sin\theta}{\cos\theta}$

$\sin^2\theta + \cos^2\theta \equiv 1$

$\sin 2\theta \equiv 2\sin\theta\cos\theta$

$\cos 2\theta \equiv \cos^2\theta - \sin^2\theta$

$\qquad = 2\cos^2\theta - 1$

$\qquad = 1 - 2\sin^2\theta$

The solutions, for domain $0° \leq x \leq 360°$, are: 30°, 150°, 210°, 330°; and 0°, 60°, 180°, 300°, 360°.

Full working can be found on the website

Finding sin from cos (and cos from sin): A simple trick is to draw a right-angled triangle. eg If $\sin\theta = \frac{3}{5}$, what is $\cos\theta$? Having put 3 as the "opposite" and 5 as the hypotenuse, the remaining side must be 4. So $\cos\theta = \frac{4}{5}$. If θ was obtuse (that is, between 90° and 180°), $\cos\theta$ would be $-\frac{4}{5}$.

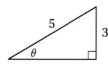

We can then go further: knowing that $\tan\theta = \frac{\sin\theta}{\cos\theta}$, $\tan\theta = \frac{3/5}{4/5} = \frac{3}{4}$, and we could also calculate $\sin2\theta = 2\sin\theta\cos\theta = 2 \times \frac{3}{5} \times \frac{4}{5} = \frac{24}{25}$.

Connection between tan θ and the gradient of a line:

The diagram shows the line with equation $y = \frac{3}{4}x$. It makes an angle θ with the x axis. Since every increment of 4 in the x direction is matched by an increment of 3 in the y direction, it follows that $\tan\theta = \frac{3}{4}$.

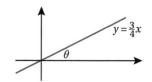

Thus the gradient of a straight line equals the tan of the angle the line makes with the horizontal.

Equations which lead to quadratics: Consider the following question:

Solve $2\cos^2 x + \sin x = 1$, $0° \le x \le 360°$ giving answers in an exact form.

We cannot solve an equation directly with sin **and** cos in it. So, using the identity $\sin^2 x + \cos^2 x = 1$, we get:

$$2(1 - \sin^2 x) + \sin x = 1 \Rightarrow 2\sin^2 x - \sin x - 1 = 0$$

This is a quadratic of equation of the form $2y^2 - y - 1 = 0$. This factorises to give $(2y + 1)(y - 1) = 0$ and thus $y = -0.5$ or 1.

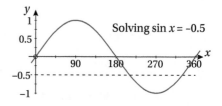

It follows that $\sin x = -0.5$ or 1, giving solutions $x = 210°$, $330°$ or $90°$.

Solving $\sin a(x + b) = k$: If $a = 2$, there will be twice as many solutions in a given range. If $a = 3$, three times as many, and so on. For example, to solve $\sin 2x = 0.5$, $0° \le x \le 360°$:

- Calculate which angles have a sin of 0.5... | 30°, 150°

- Now extend the range of angles by adding 360° ... | 390°, 510°

- These are values of $2x$. Dividing by 2 gives values of x, and brings the answers into the required range | 15°, 75°, 195°, 255°

If the problem had been to solve $\sin 2(x + 20) = 0.5$, the final solutions would be obtained by subtracting 40° from the four given above.

Exactly the same methods are used to solve equations with cos or tan.

The following question involves trigonometric identities and quadratic equations.

> (a)   Show that $4 - \cos 2x + 5\sin x = 2\sin^2 x + 5\sin x + 3$
>
> (b)   Hence solve the equation $4 - \cos 2x + 5\sin x = 0$ for $0 \leq x \leq 2\pi$

(a) $4 - \cos 2x + 5\sin x = 4 - (1 - 2\sin^2 x) + 5\sin x$ $= 2\sin^2 x + 5\sin x + 4 - 1$ $= 2\sin^2 x + 5\sin x + 3$	*(a) There are three possible formulae for cos 2x. In this case we use 1 – 2sin²x because the only function we want in the final rearrangement is sin x.*
(b) $4 - \cos 2x + 5\sin x = 0$ $2\sin 2x + 5\sin x + 3 = 0$ $(2\sin x + 3)(\sin x + 1) = 0$ $\sin x = -1$ since $\sin x = -\frac{3}{2}$ isn't possible $\therefore x = \frac{3\pi}{2}$	*(b) We now use the result of part (a) to rewrite the LHS of the equation in (b). If it helps, write the quadratic as 2y² + 5y + 3.* *sin x and cos x can only take values between –1 and 1.*

Trigonometric functions and equations: Practice Exercise

> *Only use your GDC where necessary*

1.   For $0° \leq x \leq 360°$ solve:

   (a) $\sin x = 0.75$,   (b) $\cos x = -0.5$,   (c) $\tan x = \sqrt{3}$

2.   For $-\pi \leq x \leq \pi$ solve:

   (a) $\sin x = -\frac{1}{\sqrt{2}}$,   (b) $\cos 2x = 0.5$,   (c) $\tan x = 1$

3.   Without a GDC, find values of $\sin 2\theta$ and $\cos 2\theta$ given that $\tan\theta = \frac{5}{12}$ and θ is acute.

4.   Solve the equation $3\cos 2(x - 30)° = 1.2$ for $0° \leq x \leq 180°$

5.   Show that $\cos^2\theta + \cos 2\theta = 3\cos^2\theta - 1$ and hence solve the equation $\cos^2\theta + \cos 2\theta = 0$, $0° \leq \theta \leq 360°$

Answers

1. (a) 48.6°, 131.4°
   (b) 120°, 240°
   (c) 60°, 240°

2. (a) $-\frac{\pi}{4}, -\frac{3\pi}{4}$
   (b) $-\frac{5\pi}{6}, -\frac{\pi}{6}, \frac{\pi}{6}, \frac{5\pi}{6}$
   (c) $-\frac{3\pi}{4}, \frac{\pi}{4}$

3. $\frac{120}{169}, \frac{119}{169}$

4. 63.2°, 176.8°

5. 54.7°, 125.3°, 234.7°, 305.3°

3.6 Transformations of Trigonometric Functions

The graphs of trigonometric functions can be transformed in the same way as other functions, eg:

- $y = \sin 2x$ stretches the graph of $y = \sin x$ by ½ in the x direction – this is equivalent to doubling the period or halving the wavelength.

- $y = 3\sin x$ stretches the graph ×3 in the y-direction, thus trebling the amplitude of the wave.

- $y = \sin x + 1$ moves the graph up 1 in the y-direction, thus shifting its centre of oscillation.

- If all of the above transformations were performed, in that order, on the function $f(x) = \sin x$, the transformed function would be $f(x) = 3\sin 2x + 1$ and its graph would be:

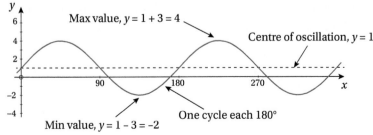

The *amplitude* of the graph is the vertical distance from the centre line to the maximum value – in this case 3.

The following two examples cover most of the techniques you will come across in exam questions. In the first one, the maximum and the minimum give us crucial information about the function.

The graph of $y = p \cos qx + r$, for $-5 \leq x \leq 11$, is shown below. A is a maximum point, B is a minimum point.

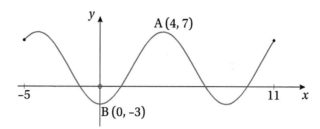

(a) Find the values of:

  (i) p

  (ii) q

  (iii) r

(b) The equation $y = k$ has exactly two solutions. Write down the value of k, given that $k < 0$.

The key to answering this question lies in the two turning points. Firstly, the difference between the y-coordinates is 10, so the amplitude of the wave is 5, and this leads us to the value of p. But note that it is an "upside down" cos graph, so p must be negative.

For $y = \cos kx$ or $y = \sin kx$, the period is $\frac{2\pi}{k}$ (or $\frac{360}{k}$ if measuring in degrees).

Looking at the two x-coordinates, we can deduce that the period (the length of one wave) is 8. This gives us the value of q (see notes box).

Finally, looking at the y-coordinates again, we can see the centre line of the wave is y = 2, and this gives us the value of r.

  (a)   (i) $p = -5$ (ii) $q = \frac{\pi}{4}$ (iii) $r = 2$

To answer questions like that in part (b), all you have to do is work out where a horizontal line added to the diagram would cut the graph in only two places. The only possibilities are a line passing through the minimum points and a line passing through the maximum points (in this question the graph only exists between x = -5 and x = 11). But k < 0, so...

  (b) $k = -3$

In the next example, which is a complete section B exam-style question, we are also given two turning points, so some of the working is the same. But the question is set within the context of a typical real-life situation (the height of the tide can be modelled by a trigonometric equation because tides are caused by the moon travelling in a circle around the Earth). It also requires a GDC.

A formula for the depth d metres of water in a harbour at time t hours after midnight is

  $d = P + Q \cos\left(\frac{\pi}{6}t\right), 0 \leq t \leq 24$

  where P and Q are positive constants. In the following graph the point $(6, 8.2)$ is a minimum point and the point $(12, 14.6)$ is a maximum point.

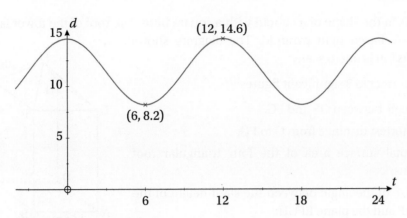

(a) Find the values of Q and P.

(b) Find the first time in the 24 hour period when the depth of water is 10 m.

(c) Use the symmetry of the graph to find the next time when the depth is 10 m, and hence the time intervals during which the water is less than 10 m deep.

(a) *The cos curve oscillates about y = 11.4 (mean of 8.2 and 14.6) and has an amplitude of 3.2 either side of this value, from which we can work out P and Q.*

$$P = 11.4, \quad Q = 3.2$$

(b) *To find when the depth is 10 we could plot the curve on the calculator and find when y = 10. Alternatively, we could solve for d = 10 as follows:*

$$10 = 11.4 + 3.2 \cos\left(\frac{\pi}{6}\right)t$$

$$\cos\left(\frac{\pi}{6}\right)t = -0.4375$$

$$\left(\frac{\pi}{6}\right)t = \arccos(-0.4375) = 2.024$$

$$t = \frac{6 \times 2.024}{\pi} = 3.87$$

So $t = 3.52$am *(Check this looks good on the graph – it does!)*

(c) *The graph is symmetrical about t = 6. 3.87 is 2.13 hours less than 6, so the next time the depth is 10m will be 2.13 more than 6. 6 + 2.13 = 8.13 hours after midnight.*

The depth will next be 10 m at 8.08am

Looking at the graph, we can see that the water is less than 10m deep between these two times and, using symmetry, it will also be less than 10m deep for 2.13 hours either side of 18.

The water will be less than 10 m for $3.87 < t < 8.13$ and $15.87 < t < 20.13$

Geometry and Trigonometry: Long Answer Questions

Starting on the next page is a selection of Section B style exam questions. The answers are given here, but full working may be found on the Peak Study Resources website.

See www.peakib.com

1. An office tower is in the shape of a cuboid with a square base. The roof of the tower is in the shape of a square based right pyramid. The diagram shows some dimensions but is not to scale.

   (a) Calculate, correct to 3 significant figures:

   (i) The angle between OF and FG;

   (ii) The shortest distance from O to FG;

   (iii) The total surface area of the four triangular roof sections;

   (iv) The size of the angle between the slant height of the roof OF and the plane EFGH;

   (v) The height of the tower from the base to O.

   (b) A parrot's nest is perched at a point, P, on the edge of BF of the tower. A person at point X, outside the building and 6 m from B, measures the angle of elevation to point P to be 79°. Find, correct to 3 significant figures, the height of the nest from the base of the tower.

   _____

   Answers:

   (a) (i) 72.5° (ii) 9.54 m (iii) 114 m² (iv) 64.9° (v) 49.1 m

   (b) 30.9 m

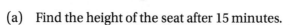

2. The London Eye is a Ferris wheel with a radius of 60 m. The diagram models the London Eye as a circle whose bottom point is 15 m above ground level. Points L, M and N represent seats at different positions on the wheel. The wheel rotates clockwise at a rate of two revolutions every hour. A seat starts at the lowest point, L.

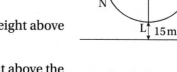

   (a) Find the height of the seat after 15 minutes.

   (b) In 5 minutes the seat moves from L to N. Find its height above the ground at this point.

   Point M is 110 m above the ground. The height of the seat above the ground after t minutes can be modelled by the function $h(t) = 60\sin(pt - q)° + 75$.

   (c) Find the value of p and the smallest value of q.

   (d) Hence find the value of t the first time the seat reaches point M.

   _____

   Answers:

   (a) 135 m

   (b) 45 m

   (c) $p = 12, q = 90$

   (d) 10.5 minutes

3. The diagram shows a quadrilateral ABCD. Angles A and C are obtuse.

   (a) Use the cosine rule to show that BD = $\sqrt{52 - 48\cos x}$

   (b) Use the sine rule to find another expression for BD in terms of x.

   (c) By equating the expressions for BD, find x.

   (d) Hence find BD.

   (e) Find y

   (f) Hence find the area of quadrilateral ABCD.

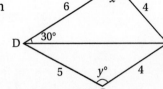

Answers:

   (b) BD = $8\sin x$

   (c) $x = 101.4°$

   (d) BD = 7.84

   (e) $y = 120.8°$

   (f) 20.4

4. (a) (i) Given that $x + 1 = \cos 2\theta$, show that $x + 2\sin^2\theta = 0$

   (ii) Given that $\dfrac{y}{\cos\theta} = \tan\theta,$ show that $y = \sin\theta$

   (iii) Hence find an expression for x in terms of y

   (iv) Given also that $x = -(y + 1)$, write down an equation for y in the form $f(y) = 0$

   (v) Solve the equation in part (iv), and hence find the corresponding values of θ between 0° and 360°.

   (b) Solve the equation $\sin^2\theta + 5\cos^2\theta = 3$ where $-180° \le \theta \le 180°$

Answers:

(a) (iii) $x = -2y^2$

   (iv) $2y^2 - y - 1 = 0$

   (v) $y = -0.5$ or 1, $\theta = 90°, 210°, 330°$

(b) $-135°, -45°, 45°, 135°$

Chapter 4: STATISTICS AND PROBABILITY

4.1 Definitions

A *population* is a set from which statistics are drawn. A *sample* is a subset drawn from the population. In a random sample, every member of the population is equally likely to be chosen. There are several different *sampling techniques*, each with advantages and disadvantages. A sampling technique may introduce *bias* – for example, selecting a sample of people in a shopping centre at 11am will not include those who are at work.

Sample statistics (such as the mean) can be used to estimate population statistics. *Discrete* data are restricted to certain values only (often integers) whereas *continuous* data can take any values. The *frequency* is the number of times a particular value occurs. When collecting data, some items may appear to be very extreme when compared to the rest of the data. Such items are called *outliers* and consideration must be given to whether they *could* be valid, or whether they are incorrect; and also how to deal with them.

Numerical data is usually collected into a *frequency table* and can then be split into *groups* or *classes*. The *boundaries* of the classes must be dealt with carefully, especially for continuous data. Consider a table of weights which begins like this:

Weight (kg)	Frequency
0–10	4
10–20	12
20–30	18

Into which class would a weight of 10kg be put? It would be better if the first group were labelled $0 \leq w < 10$ and the second $10 \leq w < 20$, then 10 would fall into the second group. The *interval width* in this case is 10, and the *mid-interval value* of the first group is 5 and so on. Data can be appreciated more when displayed in a diagram and the *frequency histogram* is the simplest way to display grouped data. A frequency histogram (often called a *bar chart*) uses equal class intervals.

4.2 Averages

Properly called "measures of central tendency", there are three types of average you need to know: mean, median and mode. An average is a single statistic which can be used to represent a whole group, although this isn't true of the mode which merely tells us the "most popular" value.

The mean: To calculate the mean, add all the numbers together and divide by the number of values, n. So mean $= \frac{\sum x_i}{n}$, where the separate values are x_1, x_2, x_3 and so on. The symbol for sample mean is $\bar{x}$. Note that $n\bar{x} = \sum x_i$.

Example: In 9 games I have scored a mean of 12.8 points. In the 10th game I score 16 points – what is my new mean?

Solution: The total score in the first 9 games is $9 \times 12.8 = 115.2$. My new total in 10 games is $115.2 + 16 = 131.2$, so my new mean is $\frac{131.2}{10} = 13.12$.

Here's a similar question:

100 people are staying at a hotel: 68 are men and 32 women. The men have a mean height of 1.75 m and the women have a mean height of 1.64 m. Find the mean height of the 100 people.

The answer is 1.71 m.

If you can't get there, you'll find full working on the website.

If the data is in a frequency table – such as the one below showing how many pupils were absent during a month – then the total value is calculated by multiplying each value by its frequency and summing the results.

Pupils absent (x)	No of days (f)	fx
0	20	0
1	4	4
2	3	6
3	3	9
TOTAL	30	19

There were a total of 19 days absence over a period of 30 days. So the mean number of absences per day was $\frac{19}{30} = 0.63$. (It is a common mistake to divide 19 by 4, the number of classes).

If the data is presented in a **grouped** frequency table, the same procedure is followed except that the mid-interval value of each group is used to represent the x value for each group. This means that the **actual** data values are unknown and in this case the mean is only an estimate.

Weight of apples (w)	No of apples (f)	Mid interval	fx
$20 \leq w < 25$	12	22.5	270
$25 \leq w < 30$	20	27.5	550
$30 \leq w < 35$	25	32.5	812.5
$35 \leq w < 40$	17	37.5	637.5
TOTAL	74		2270

Estimated mean weight of an apple is $\frac{2270}{74} = 30.7$ g.

Always check if the answer is "reasonable." Look at the distribution of weights – does 30.7 **look** like the mean?

The table shows the scores of competitors in a competition.

Score	10	20	30	40	50
Number of competitors with this score	1	2	5	k	3

The mean score is 34. Find the value of k.

Total score $= 10 + 40 + 150 + 40k + 150 = 350 + 40k$

Number of competitors $= 1 + 2 + 5 + k + 3 = 11 + k$

Mean is $\dfrac{350 + 40k}{11 + k} = 34$

$350 + 40k = 34(11 + k)$

$350 + 40k = 374 + 34k$

$6k = 24$

$k = 4$

At first sight you may be puzzled as to how to tackle a question like this. But, knowing the formula for the mean, just carry on and see what happens!

If you find the algebra too much, you can of course use the equation-solving functionality of your GDC.

Your GDC will calculate the mean of a set of numbers within its statistical functions. But be careful: if you want the mean of a frequency table you will need two lists (the values and the frequencies), and the GDC will need to know that the second list contains the frequencies. If you're uncertain about this, try it with the table above.

In general, if there are n values, the median is in the $\dfrac{n+1}{2}$th position.

Median: If a set of values is listed in order, the middle value is the *median*. It is another type of average: there are as many values above the median as below it. Unlike the mean, it is unaffected by particularly large or small values. In the following list there are 15 values so the 8th is the middle one (7 below it, 7 above it).

$$1\ \ 1\ \ 3\ \ 5\ \ 6\ \ 6\ \ 6\ \ \underline{7}\ \ 7\ \ 9\ \ 10\ \ 10\ \ 12\ \ 15\ \ 18 \rightarrow \text{median} = 7$$

If there is an even number of values, find the mean of the middle two to calculate the median.

$$24\ \ 26\ \ 27\ \ \underline{27\ \ 29}\ \ 30\ \ 30\ \ 33 \rightarrow \text{median} = 28$$

If the data is in the form of a frequency table, then the calculation depends on whether it is discrete or continuous.

Discrete distribution

Beware! If you enter a grouped frequency table, you will *not* get correct values for the median and the quartiles.

x	1	2	3	4	5	6
f	4	11	17	25	14	4

There are 75 values, so the median will be the 38th. The first 4 values are 1s, the next 11 are 2s, making 15 values so far. Another 17 are 3s making 32 values. So the 38th value must be in the next box, and thus the median is 4.

Continuous distribution

x	0 –	5 –	10 –	15 –	20 –	25 – 30
f	4	11	17	25	14	4

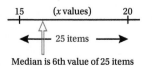

Median is 6th value of 25 items

This time, the values are spread throughout each class, so the 38th value will be the 6th in the class 15–20. Interpolating, median $= 15 + \dfrac{6}{25} \times 5 = 16.2$

Cumulative frequency tables: It is slightly easier to estimate the median from a frequency table if it is first converted into a *cumulative frequency table*. Whether the data is discrete or continuous, the method is the same. Each value of cumulative frequency measures how many x values there are in total up to that point. The two tables above convert into the following:

x	≤ 1	≤ 2	≤ 3	≤ 4	≤ 5	≤ 6
Cumul. f	4	15	32	57	71	75

In the first table we can see that there are 32 values up to 3, so the 38th value must be contained in the next group and is 4.

x	<5	<10	<15	<20	<25	<30
Cumul. f	4	15	32	57	71	75

Note that in the conversion of the grouped frequency table, the "up to" points are the **top** of each group.

In the second table we have to recalculate the fact that there are 25 values in the group 15–20, and then go on to the calculation shown above.

The advantage here is not so great, but we can go one stage further and draw a cumulative frequency graph to help us.

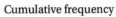

The points in the table are plotted and are joined either by straight lines or a smooth curve. To find the median, a line is drawn to the right from 38 (the middle value of the distribution) and down to the x-axis.

The median can be seen to be about 16.

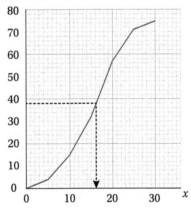

Quartiles: 50% of the population lie above the median, 50% below. We can also divide the population into *quartiles*: 25% lie below the first quartile, 50% below the second (which is also the median) 75% below the third quartile. There are 75 results in the previous table, so the first quartile will be the 19th result. Looking at the graph, this gives the first quartile as 11 and the third quartile (the 57th result) as 20. Similarly, the distribution can be divided into 100 parts knows as *percentiles*. "Your test result is in the top 5 percentiles of the population" means that at least 95% of people scored worse than you did.

There are various methods for calculating quartiles of a discrete distribution. For the exam, you will be expected either to use a graph or your GDC

Mode: The mode, or modal value, is simply the value which occurs the most often in a frequency distribution. In other words, the value with the greatest frequency. In a grouped frequency distribution, the group with the greatest frequency is called the *modal class*. Note that there can be more than one modal value or class.

Puzzle: Can you find five numbers such that mode < median < mean? And can you find five numbers such that mode < mean < median?

Solution: There are lots of possibilities, such as 2, 2, 5, 10, 12 and 2, 2, 6, 7, 8.

4.3 Measures of spread

The mean gives an indication of the "centre" of the distribution. The next most important statistic is a measure of "spread." For example, a buyer in a crisp factory testing different packing machines would be interested to know the mean number of crisps each machine put into bags, but it is equally important to know how *consistent* the machines are.

Standard deviation: The *standard deviation* provides a measure of how much results deviate, on average, from the mean.

Make sure you understand how to enter a frequency table into your calculator and how to obtain results for the mean and standard deviation.

> To save my typing fingers, I shall use SD as an abbreviation for standard deviation.

Try calculating the SD of weight of peanuts in these 80 packets:

Weight	No of packets
$80 \leq W < 85$	5
$85 \leq W < 90$	10
$90 \leq W < 95$	15
$95 \leq W < 100$	26
$100 \leq W < 105$	13
$105 \leq W < 110$	7
$110 \leq W < 115$	4

You should find that the mean weight is 96.8 and the standard deviation is 7.41.

As a rough indicator, the majority of results in a reasonably symmetrical distribution are within two standard deviations of the mean (ie $\bar{x} \pm 2SD$). For example, a class takes a mathematics test. The mean score is 65% and the standard deviation is 8%. This means that most scores will be in the range 65 ± 16, ie 49% to 81%.

The *variance* is a useful statistic for further calculations, but does not have much significance on its own. It is the square of the standard deviation.

Outliers: The "two standard deviation test" gives us a useful way of identifying outliers.

Example: The following times, in seconds, were recorded in a race:

> 140, 148, 152, 155, 156, 156, 157, 160, 162, 162, 165, 170.

> What evidence is there to suggest that 140 s was an exceptionally fast time for this group?

Solution: Using a GDC, mean = 156.9 and SD = 7.60, so 2SD below the mean is 141.7. Therefore, 140 s is an outlier and can be classed as "exceptionally fast."

In the previous example this doesn't mean that the result can be discounted – some genuine results will be outliers. However, if the result had been recorded as 14 s this is clearly an error and should not be included in the data set.

Effect of changes to the data: Take a group of 10 children whose mean age is 12.4 years. What will be their mean age in 5 years' time? Since each of their ages will have had 5 added on, the mean will have increased by the same amount and will therefore be 17.4 years.

And how will the standard deviation have changed? Not at all, since the *spread* of their ages around the mean will be exactly the same.

However, suppose a group of people take an exam marked out of 50; the mean is 35.2, and the standard deviation is 6.1. The scores are turned into percentages by doubling: the mean will now be 70.4, and the SD will have doubled as well to 12.2 since the marks will all have doubled their distance from the mean.

Thus, if a set of data has mean m and SD s, then the following rules apply:

- Add a to each of the data values: the mean will be $m + a$, and the SD will be s.
- Multiply each of the data values by b: the mean will be mb, and the SD will be sb.

These rules can be combined. If a set of data is doubled, and then 5 added on, the mean will be $2m + 5$ and the SD will be $2s$.

Interquartile range: The standard deviation of a distribution gives us a measure of the spread of the results which is calculated using each of the values. A cruder measure of the spread is the *interquartile range* which is calculated by subtracting the lower quartile from the upper quartile. Effectively, it tells us the spread of results for the middle 50% of the population. In questions, you will normally find the standard deviation "paired" with the mean, and the IQR paired with the median.

Not to be confused with the range, which is simply the difference between the maximum and minimum values.

A survey is carried out to find the waiting time of 100 customers in a post office.

(a) Calculate an estimate of the mean waiting time.

(b) Construct a cumulative frequency table for the data.

(c) Use the table in (b) to draw a cumulative frequency graph, using a scale of 1 cm per 20 seconds on the horizontal axis and 1 cm per 10 customers on the vertical axis.

(d) Use the cumulative frequency graph to find estimates for the median and interquartile range.

(e) Use the graph to estimate how many people waited more than 115 seconds.

Waiting time (sec)	Number of customers
0–20	5
20–40	18
40–60	30
60–80	22
80–100	9
100–120	7
120–140	6
140–160	3

(a) Mean = 64.4 (GDC)

(b)

Waiting time (sec)	Cumulative frequency
≤ 20	5
≤ 40	23
≤ 60	53
≤ 80	75
≤ 100	84
≤ 120	91
≤ 140	97
≤ 160	100

(c)

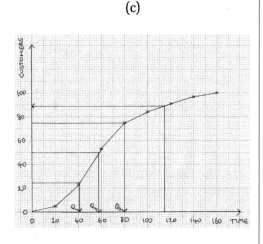

(d) Median (also known as Q_2) = 58

Lower quartile (Q_1) = 41, Upper quartile (Q_3) = 80, IQR = 80 – 41 = 39

(e) 100 – 89 = 11 people waited more than 115 minutes

You must draw the relevant lines on the graph to show how you arrive at your answers. You will be given a little leeway with the numbers, but try to be as accurate as possible.

Outliers (again): Since the IQR is a measure of spread we can also use it to define outliers. A well-used definition of an outlier is a data value which is more than $1.5 \times$ IQR above the upper quartile, or below the lower quartile.

In the question above, $Q_1 - 1.5 \times$ IQR $= 41 - 1.5 \times 39 = -17.5$, so it is impossible for there to be outliers at the lower end of the distribution. But $Q_3 + 1.5 \times$ IQR $= 80 + 1.5 \times 39 = 138.5$: any values above 138.5 can be considered as outliers. We know that there must be at least 3 outliers since there are 3 values above 140 minutes.

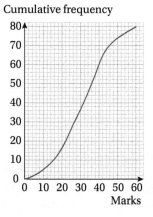

Example: The cumulative frequency diagram shows the marks out of 70 gained by 80 students in a test. Write down the median, the quartiles and the IQR. One student took the test late and gained 66 marks – is this an outlier?

Solution: Median = 32, Q_1 = 22, Q_3 = 40, IQR = 40 – 22 = 18.

Outliers would be greater than 40 + 27 = 67. Therefore, the mark is not an outlier.

An outlier would be indicated by a cross.

Box and Whisker plots: A box and whisker plot is a useful device for illustrating some key statistics for a distribution. The ends of the box represent the lower and upper quartiles, and the ends of the "whiskers" the extreme values. The median is shown by a line inside the box. A scale is drawn below the box and whisker plot, and different distributions can be compared. The illustration below shows the box and whisker plots for two math exams taken by a group of students.

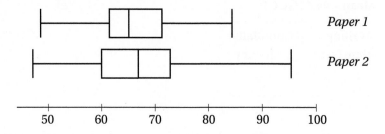

A question may ask you to compare the distributions – simple statements will suffice. For example:

- The range of results on Paper 1 is smaller.
- The median mark of the two papers is about the same.
- The interquartile range on Paper 2 is larger.

Averages and Spread: Practice Exercise

1. The following table shows the number of errors per page in a 100 page document.

Number of errors	0	1	2	3	4	5
Number of pages	28	22	18	14	12	6

    (a) State whether the data is discrete or continuous.

    (b) Draw a bar chart to represent the data.

    (c) Find the mean number of errors per page.

    (d) Find the median number of errors per page.

    (e) Write down the modal number of errors per page.

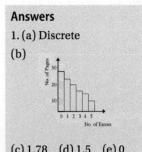
2. The cumulative frequency graph has been drawn from a frequency table showing the time it takes two hundred students to complete a computer game.

    (a) Find the median.

    (b) Find the interquartile range.

The graph has been drawn using the data in the following frequency table:

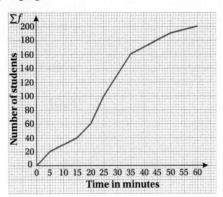

Time (min)	$0 < x \le 5$	$5 < x \le 15$	$15 < x \le 20$	$20 < x \le 25$	$25 < x \le 35$	$35 < x \le 50$	$50 < x \le 60$
No. of students	20	20	a	40	60	b	10

    (c) Using the graph, find the values of a and b.

    (d) Calculate an estimate of the mean time taken to complete the computer game.

3. The bar chart shows the number of hours a professional musician practises each day during April:

    (a) Write down the modal number of hours.

    (b) Calculate the mean number of hours he practises each day.

    (c) Find the standard deviation.

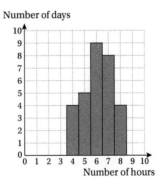

4. The following diagram is a box and whisker plot (not to scale) for a set of data. The interquartile range is 15 and the range is 50.

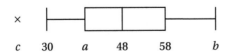

    (a) Write down the median value.

    (b) Find the values of a and b.

    (c) The cross represents an outlier. What is the highest possible integer value for c?

4.4 Correlation

Scatter diagrams: Two sets of data which appear to have a relationship between them are said to be *correlated*. For example, a company may find that there is a direct relationship between the amount it spends on advertising and its sales figures. Note that correlation does not imply causality: the correlation may be coincidental, or it may be linked to a third factor (perhaps, in this case, differing economic conditions).

A simple way to assess possible correlation is to draw a *scatter diagram*. The two sets of data are plotted on a standard *x-y* graph (but not joined in any way).

Qualitative conclusions which can be drawn about the correlation are:

> It is not necessary for the axes in a scatter diagram to be labelled from 0. We are only interested in the relationship between the points.

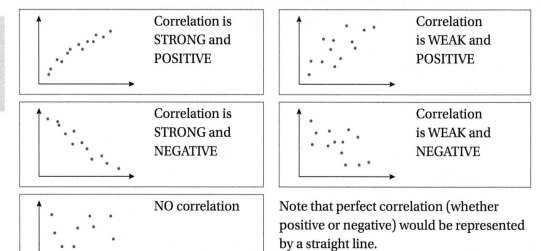

Correlation is STRONG and POSITIVE

Correlation is WEAK and POSITIVE

Correlation is STRONG and NEGATIVE

Correlation is WEAK and NEGATIVE

NO correlation

Note that perfect correlation (whether positive or negative) would be represented by a straight line.

Let's look at a couple of examples:

In this first one, a group of 10 to 16 year old boys were timed running 100m. We can see that there is strong negative correlation between their ages and their times.

Do you think that you can extrapolate to estimate the time taken by a 21 year old? A 60 year old?

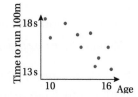

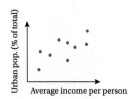

In this second graph, we are comparing countries by the percentage who live in cities against the average income per person in each country. Quite strong correlation – but, again, could we extrapolate and say that the figures will always increase together?

The answer in both cases is "no." In the first example, extrapolation would indicate that a 40 year old could run 100 m in 0 seconds! I would expect the graph to begin to turn soon, and then start back up again. In the second example, it's possible that extrapolation would work for a short distance (although we haven't been given scales); however, no country can have more than 100% of its people living in cities.

Line of best fit: A scatter diagram indicates the relationship between two variables. If we conclude that there *is* a relationship, we can draw in the "line of best fit" by eye and then use this to predict more pairs of values. If you know the mean values of the two variables, the line of best fit should pass through the point $(\bar{x}, \bar{y})$. Note that

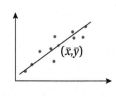

although *interpolation* (ie putting new points in between existing points) is fairly safe, *extrapolation* (ie continuing the line beyond the existing points) may not be valid. There may be reasons why the relationship does not continue in the same way.

Correlation Coefficient: For a quantitative assessment of correlation we can calculate the *product-moment coefficient,* denoted by r. This is derived from all the pairs of values and has the following properties:

- A coefficient of –1 indicates perfect negative correlation.
- A coefficient of 0 indicates no correlation.
- A coefficient of +1 indicates perfect positive correlation.

The size of r (ie the positive value of r) indicates the strength of the correlation, but this also depends on the number of pairs of values. However, we can say generally that:

- $0.25 \leq r < 0.5 \Rightarrow$ weak correlation
- $0.5 \leq r < 0.75 \Rightarrow$ moderate correlation
- $0.75 \leq r < 1 \Rightarrow$ strong correlation

(and similarly for negative values of r).

Using your calculator: Although you may have learnt how to calculate the equation of the line of best fit (or *regression line*) and also correlation coefficients using formulae, you will not be expected to do this in the exam. However, you should be able to do both of these things using your GDC. Generally, the method is to input the pairs of x and y values, then use the appropriate calculator functions.

Check that you are able to carry out these calculations using the following data:

x	2	4	5	7	9	10	11	15
y	3	4	6	6	7	9	10	11

You should find that the correlation coefficient is 0.97 (not surprising when you look at how closely the y values follow the x values) and that the regression line of y on x has equation $y = 1.89 + 0.65x$.

The equation of the line can be used to predict further data points. For example, what is the likely value of y when $x = 7.8$, and when $x = 17$?

When $x = 7.8$, $y = 1.89 + 0.65 \times 7.8 = 6.96$

When $x = 17$, $y = 1.89 + 0.65 \times 17 = 12.94$

Because the regression line is "y on x" it can only be used to calculate y values given x values.

If you are given the equation of an "x on y" regression line, that can be used to calculate x values.

However, as mentioned earlier, the latter result must be treated with caution since it has been extrapolated beyond the end of the known data – there is no guarantee that the relationship between x and y will continue to hold.

Since the equation of the regression line is a linear function, the values of a and b can represent physical quantities. a is the gradient, so represents "y quantity per x quantity". And b is the y-intercept, so represents the value when $x = 0$, which is less likely to be meaningful. Using the first example above (time to run 100 m versus age in years), a would represent "time to run 100 m per year"; in other words, how much faster a boy would run for every extra year in age. b would represent "time to run 100 m at age 0" which is clearly a nonsense; in any case, the data is only valid between ages 10 and 16.

The following table shows the amount of fuel (y litres) used by a car to travel certain distances (x km).

Distance (x km)	50	80	125	160	195
Fuel (y litres)	4.6	7.1	10.9	13.9	16.9

This data can be modelled by the regression line with equation $y = ax + b$.

(a) (i) Find the values of a and b.

(ii) Explain what the gradient a represents.

(b) Use the model to estimate the amount of fuel used to drive 100 km.

(c) Could the model be used to estimate the amount of fuel to drive 250 km?

a) (i) $a = 0.085$, $b = 0.326$

(ii) litres/km travelled

b) 8.82

c) Yes, because fuel usage doesn't change with distance.

OR

No, because this would involve extrapolating beyond the data range.

a) It's very easy to test whether your answer is correct – just try using the formula on one of the x values and check you get the corresponding y value (or something close to it).

c) Either answer would do – as long as you give a valid explanation. But it's perhaps safer to always say no to extrapolation.

Piecewise models: When a function is graphed as separate line segments, meeting at common points, it is known as a *piecewise linear function* (see figure on right). Sometimes correlation on a scatter diagram would be better achieved with more than one line of best fit, in which case we end up with a piecewise model. In other words, a single regression line may fit reasonably well, but two (or more) would fit the points much more closely.

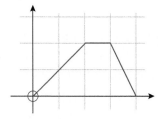

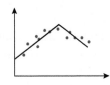

Here's an example of a piecewise model with two clearly defined sections. It's important that the point where the lines join satisfies the equations of both of the two regression lines. What sort of situations might give rise to a piecewise model? Well, the scatter diagram could represent measures of air pollution at different distances from a city centre. Moving out from the centre we pass through an increasingly industrialised zone with greater pollution; and then further out in the suburbs, so pollution decreases.

Example: A piecewise linear model contains two regression lines with equations $y = 1.6x + 2$ for $0 \leq x \leq 2$, $y = 7 - 0.9x$ for $2 \leq x \leq 5$. Find the point where the two lines meet, and also calculate y values when $x = 0.8$ and when $x = 3.5$.

Solution: Solving the two equations simultaneously (GDC) we find the lines meet at (2, 5.2). When $x = 0.8$ (first section), $y = 4.28$. When $x = 3.5$ (second section), $y = 3.85$.

Or you can tell from the domains in the question that the two lines meet when $x = 2$.

64

4.5 Sampling Methods

Ideally, statistics are gathered from a whole population. In practice, this is usually too expensive and too time-consuming, so a population sample is used instead. The difficulty is to make the sample representative of the population, so that conclusions drawn from the sample can be applied to the population.

"Population" doesn't just refer to people. For example, a machine in a factory may turn out 1000 components in a day. From this population, the quality control manager may want to select a sample of 20 components to test – how should he set about it?

One of the aims of sampling is to introduce as little bias as possible.

- Standing on a street corner at 11am selecting people for a survey introduces bias because the majority of the sample will not include people who are employed.

- Asking people to review a restaurant online with the promise of a possible discount introduces bias because people are more likely to give a good review.

- Selecting all 20 components (for the quality control test) in the morning may introduce bias because the machine could become more erratic later in the day.

Simple random sampling: The definition of a simple random sample is that every member of the population is equally likely to be chosen for the sample. Suppose you want a sample of 25 employees to be chosen from a company employing 300. Write all 300 names on pieces of paper, put them in a box, and then pull out 25 names. Every employee is thus equally likely to be in the sample. What this method will not achieve is a sample which reflects the make-up of the population: the male/female split, the number of employees in each age group and so on. By chance, the sample might contain all women aged between 25 and 30.

> Instead of pieces of paper, every employee could be allocated a number, and then the sample is selected using a computerised random number generator.

Convenience sampling: In this method of sampling, data is collected from population members who are conveniently available. In other words, no inclusion criteria are specified before sampling takes place. Its main purpose is to gain some initial data prior to a proper study taking place – for example, to obtain a perception of an image brand by simply going up to people in the street and asking their opinion.

Systematic sampling: Returning to our factory producing 1000 components a day, a simple way of selecting a sample of 20 is to choose every 50th component off the production line. If the first sample is chosen randomly from the first 50 components, then this ensures every component has an equal chance of being chosen. The main disadvantage of this method is that we need to know the population size to begin with. If, for example, a researcher wants to study a sample of 20 trees in a forest, she cannot systematically choose them without knowing how many trees there are in total.

Quota sampling: Quota sampling is used to select members of a population which has been divided into sub-groups. For example, a researcher wants to gather data on males and females, further sub-divided into age under 21 or 21 and over. He requires 30 of each (ie a sample size of 120), and simply approaches people until he has fulfilled each quota. This method is used if time or funding is limited but, since the sample is not genuinely random, the data is unreliable. Further bias could be introduced because the researcher may only question people who look approachable.

Stratified sampling: This method is the same as quota sampling except that within each group the sample is chosen by a method such as simple random sampling. For example, a school has 460 boys and 540 girls. A representative sample of 50 is to be chosen using stratified sampling. 50 is $\frac{1}{20}$ of the whole school, so we need to choose $\frac{1}{20} \times 460 = 23$ boys and $\frac{1}{20} \times 540 = 27$ girls. Now put all the boys' names in a box and choose 23 of them, then do the same for the 27 girls. Alternatively, go down the school list choosing every 20th boy and every 20th girl.

Stratified sampling will be used, for example, when it is important to an opinion pollster to gather results according to gender, age, political persuasion, and employment type.

The top two year groups in a school (Year 12 and Year 13) are to take part in a survey about the future of school uniform. The 200 pupils are divided by gender and year group as follows:

	Male	Female
Year 12	55	50
Year 13	48	47

A sample group of 30 are to be chosen. How would you select the group using stratified sampling?

There are 200 pupils in the group. $30 \div 200 = 0.15$.

Year 12 male = $0.15 \times 55 = 8.25$ Select 8.

Year 12 female = $0.15 \times 50 = 7.5$ Select 8.

Year 13 male = $0.15 \times 48 = 7.2$ Select 7.

Year 13 female = $0.15 \times 47 = 7.05$ Select 7.

Now allocate numbers to each of the members of the group, for example Year 12 males from 01 to 55, and use a random number generator to select the appropriate number from each group.

If the numbers don't come out as integers, it is important to ensure that the sample size from each group still adds up to the overall sample size. In this case I rounded 7.5 up to 8 to ensure the total was 30.

Any method of random sampling can be used for the second part.

4.6 Probability Notation and Formulae

Notation: The *sample space* in a given situation is the set of all the things that can happen and is defined by the letter U. An *event* is one of the things that can happen and is given any other capital letter. A capital P stands for "probability", so we can shorten "the probability of event A" to P(A). The number of ways A can happen is denoted by $n(A)$. Probabilities are always numbers between 0 (definitely won't happen) and 1 (definitely will happen). The probability that A happens is given by $P(A) = \frac{n(A)}{n(U)}$. The probability that event A does **not** happen is denoted by A'. It follows that $P(A) + P(A') = 1$.

The set notation symbols $\cap$ and $\cup$ are used for the words "and" and "or" in probability.

Combined events: The probability of event A *or* event B happening (and this includes both) is calculated using addition.

- $P(A \cup B) = P(A) + P(B)$

but this formula works **only** if A and B are *mutually exclusive* – ie they cannot both happen. If they are not mutually exclusive, use:

- $P(A \cup B) = P(A) + P(B) - P(A \cap B)$

The probability of events A and B **both** happening is calculated by multiplication (remember that multiplying fractions gives a **smaller** answer and it is **less** likely that both events will happen than just one).

- $P(A \cap B) = P(A) \times P(B)$

but this formula works **only** if A and B are *independent* – ie one of them happening does not affect the probability of the other happening. If the events are not independent we are into the realms of *conditional probability* – ie the probability of one event happening if another has already happened. This is written as $P(A|B)$, and read as "the probability of A given B."

- $P(A|B) = \dfrac{P(A \cap B)}{P(B)}$

> A bag contains balls of two different colours. One is taken out, then another. The colour of the second is independent of the first if the first has been put back. If the first has been kept out, the colour of the second *depends* on the colour of the first.

Note that the definition of independence is $P(A) = P(A|B) = P(A|B')$ (in other words, the probability of A is the same whether or not B has happened). But if you are asked to test whether events are independent, the normal test is to check if $P(A \cap B) = P(A) \times P(B)$.

For the events A and B, $P(A) = 0.3$, $P(B) = 0.4$.

    (a)   Find $P(A \cup B)$ if A and B are independent events.

    (b)   Find $P(A' \cap B')$ if A and B are mutually exclusive events.

(a) $P(A \cap B) = 0.3 \times 0.4 = 0.12$
        $P(A \cup B) = P(A) + P(B) - P(A \cap B)$
                $= 0.3 + 0.4 - 0.12$
                $= 0.58$
	(a) We are not told the events are mutually exclusive so we must use the full formula or P(A or B). This involves P(A and B) which we can calculate because they are independent.

(b) $P(A \cup B) = P(A) + P(B) = 0.7$ So, $P(A' \cap B') = 1 - P(A \cup B) = 0.3$	*(b) is a new question so we cannot use independence. You will see in the next section how a Venn diagram can help you solve these sorts of problems more easily.*

The formulae can be quite difficult to use, so only use them if you **have** to. Many probability questions can be solved by using appropriate diagrams as shown on the next few pages.

4.7 Lists and Tables of Outcomes

Lists: A list of possible outcomes is useful if there aren't too many of them; and it is important to ensure that each outcome in the list is equally likely. For example, when three coins are thrown, the possible combinations of heads and tails are:

HHH, HHT, HTH, HTT, THH, THT, TTH, TTT

If we want to find P(exactly two heads) we can see that there are three ways of achieving this (HHT, HTH, THH) so the probability is 3/8.

Possibility Space diagram: This is a way of showing a list of outcomes on a diagram, but can only be used for two events. For example, the diagram below shows all the possible totals when two six-sided dice (red and green) are thrown:

Note that there is only one way a double 2, say, can happen – a 2 on the green and a 2 on the red. But a 1 and a 3 can happen in two ways: 1 on the green and 3 on the red, or the other way around.

Green							
6	6	7	8	9	10	11	12
5	5	6	7	8	9	10	11
4	4	5	6	7	8	9	10
3	3	4	5	6	7	8	9
2	2	3	4	5	6	7	8
1	1	2	3	4	5	6	7
		1	**2**	**3**	**4**	**5**	**6**

Red

Thus there are 36 possibilities. Some examples of probabilities are:

$$P(\text{Total of 5}) = 4/36$$

$$P(\text{Total of 5 or 7}) = 10/36$$

$$P(\text{Total of 4 or a double}) = 8/36$$

$$P(\text{Double}|\text{total} \geq 9) = 2/10$$

The conditional probability in the last example is easy to see on the diagram. We *know* that the total is ≥ 9, and there are 10 ways this can have happened. Of these, 2 could be a double.

Tables of outcomes: Tables of outcomes show how many ways two events can, or cannot, happen. For example, let's take a survey of 200 people of whom 90 are female. 60 people were unemployed, including 20 males. Filling that information into a table of outcomes, we get:

	Males	Females	Totals
Unemployed	20		60
Employed			
Totals		90	200

You will see that there is just enough information to allow us to fill in the rest of the table. Try it before looking at the answer below.

	Males	Females	Totals
Unemployed	20	40	60
Employed	90	50	140
Totals	110	90	200

Now, if a person is selected at random from the 200, what is the probability that the person is (a) an unemployed female, (b) a male, given that the person is employed.

(a) There are 40 unemployed females out of 200, so

$$P(\text{unemployed female}) = \frac{40}{200}.$$

(b) Knowing that the person is employed, he/she must be one of the 140. Of these 90 are males, so $P(\text{male}|\text{employed}) = \frac{90}{140}$. As with the possibility space diagram, it is easy to deal with conditional probability when using a table of outcomes.

4.8 Venn Diagrams

In a room there are 20 people. 11 have black hair, 6 have glasses. 2 people have both black hair and glasses. Imagine that we draw two circles on the floor labelled "black hair" and "glasses" and ask the people to stand in the appropriate circle. The circles will have to overlap to allow for the two people with both. The numbers of people in each region of the room will be:

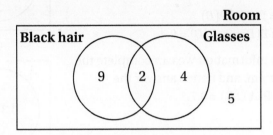

This is the same as a Venn Diagram. The "room" represents the sample space – for a particular question, there is nothing outside. Each circle represents a set, the overlap is the intersection.

Some examples of Venn Diagrams are shown below:

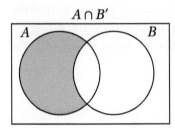
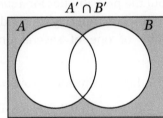
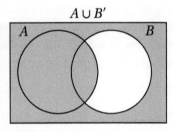

Points to note when filling in the numbers in a Venn Diagram:

- Start at the centre. If you are not told how many in the intersection, work it out like this: suppose you know there are 15 people in total in the two circles, 10 in circle A and 8 in circle B. 10 + 8 = 18, 3 more than 15, so there are 3 in the intersection.

- When we were told that there were 11 people with black hair, this *includes* those with both black hair and glasses. Same with the 6 people with glasses.

- Don't forget to fill in the outer region – although in some questions this set will be "empty."

Probabilities can now be calculated easily. When someone is selected at random, the probability they have:

Black hair and glasses = 2/20

Black hair and no glasses = 9/20

Not got glasses = 14/20

Glasses or black hair (or both) = 15/20

Glasses given black hair = 2/11

Glasses given not black hair = 4/9

Venn Diagrams are very helpful when calculating conditional probability – you may like to look at an article I have written for a fuller explanation.

See www.peakib.com

The next example shows how a Venn diagram can be used as an alternative to using the formulae.

Example: A and B are independent events. $P(A \cap B) = 0.2$, $P(A \cap B') = 0.3$

Find $P(A \cup B)$.

Solution: Intersections are easy to draw on a Venn diagram – see right.

Now we note that A and B are independent so we can use the formula

$P(A \cap B) = P(A) \times P(B)$.
$0.2 = 0.5 \times P(B) \Rightarrow P(B) = 0.4$

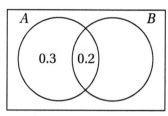

Using this information we can complete the Venn diagram, and hence answer the question: $P(A \cup B) = 0.7$.

We can answer most questions once we have a complete Venn diagram. For example, can you show that $P(A|B) = 0.5$ and also that $P(B'|A) = 0.6$

4.9 Tree Diagrams

Tree diagrams are used to work out the probabilities for a *succession* of events. To find the probability of a set of successive branches, multiply each individual probability *along* the branches. To find the probability of one of several branches occurring, add the probabilities of each outcome.

Note that the probabilities associated with, say, taking two balls out of a bag simultaneously are the same as if the balls were taken out consecutively.

eg: P(rains today) = 0.3. If it rains today, P(rains tomorrow) = 0.65

However, if it is dry today, P(rains tomorrow) = 0.2 The tree diagram which shows the full set of possible outcomes and their associated probabilities is:

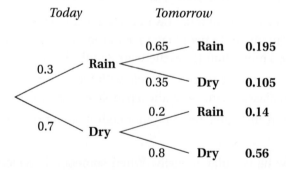

Note the following points:

- Probabilities of branches coming out of one point add to give 1 since they cover all possibilities.
- The overall probabilities also add to give 1.
- The weather tomorrow is **not** independent of the weather today, hence the different probabilities depending on today's weather.

Some example probabilities are:

- P(two rainy days) = 0.195
- P(at least one rainy day) = 0.195 + 0.105 + 0.14 = 0.44
$$= 1 - \text{P(two dry days)}$$
- P(exactly one rainy day) = 0.105 + 0.14 = 0.245

Questions about tree diagrams often come with a sting in the tail in the form of a conditional probability problem. Consider the following tree diagram where event A = "my alarm clock works" and event L = "I am late for school."

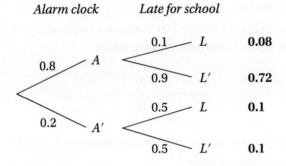

$$\text{Alarm clock} \qquad \text{Late for school}$$

$$P(\text{I am late for school}) = P(L|A) + P(L|A') = 0.08 + 0.1 = 0.18.$$

But suppose I am late for school, and my teacher says: "Obviously your alarm clock didn't work", what is the probability she is right?

The calculation is $P(A'|L) = \dfrac{P(A' \cap L)}{P(L)} = \dfrac{0.1}{0.18} = 0.556$. Another way to think of this is to consider the expected values over 100 days. On 18 of them we would expect to be late, and of these 18 we would expect the alarm clock to have failed on 10.

The probability that it is sunny in Bonn is 0.6. The probability that a girl passes a test is 0.7 when it is sunny and 0.3 when it is not sunny.

(a) Create a tree diagram to represent the above information.

(b) What is the probability that the girl passes the test on any given day?

(c) Given that a girl passes the test, what is the probability that it is sunny in Bonn?

(b) 0.54 (c) 0.778

See worked solution online

Expected number of occurrences: In the previous example about alarm clocks, I suggested looking at the number of times I would expect to be late over a period of 100 days. $P(\text{late}) = 0.18$, so I would expect to be late on $0.18 \times 100 = 18$ days. This is a specific example of a simple calculation: whenever you have the probability p of an event, and that event could happen on n occasions, the expected number of occurrences is pn.

4.10 Discrete Probability Distributions

A probability distribution shows the probabilities for all the outcomes of a particular event. Discrete probability distributions relate to events which can only have certain outcomes – usually in the form of integers.

Uniform distributions: If all the outcomes are equally likely, the distribution is called *uniform*. For example, here is the probability distribution for the random variable X where X represents the outcomes when throwing a die.

Note that the capital letter X is used to describe the random variable, whereas lower case x is used to represent the actual values.

x	1	2	3	4	5	6
$P(X = x)$	1/6	1/6	1/6	1/6	1/6	1/6

Distributions defined by a function: The following is an example of a probability distribution defined by a function:

$$P(X = x) = \begin{cases} kx, & x = 1, 2, 3, 4, 5 \\ 0 & \text{otherwise} \end{cases}$$

This means that x can only take values 1 to 5, and has probability kx for these values. The best thing to do is put all the information into a table:

x	1	2	3	4	5
$P(X = x)$	k	$2k$	$3k$	$4k$	$5k$

In all probability distributions, the probabilities add to give 1, so $15k = 1$, giving $k = \frac{1}{15}$. We can fill the probabilities into the table:

x	1	2	3	4	5
$P(X = x)$	$\frac{1}{15}$	$\frac{2}{15}$	$\frac{3}{15}$	$\frac{4}{15}$	$\frac{5}{15}$

Expected value (mean): By multiplying each value of x by its associated probability, we obtain the *expected mean*. Thus the formula is: $E(X) = \sum xp$. In the above example we get $\frac{55}{15} = 3.67$, and the more times we carry out the trial, the closer the ***actual*** mean will get to this value.

Example: The probability distribution for a random variable X is given by:

$P(X = x) = kx(x - 1)$, for $x = 2, 3, 4, 5, 6$

(a) Find the value of k; (b) Find the expected mean of the distribution.

Solution: First we must draw up the probability table:

x	2	3	4	5	6
$P(X = x)$	$2k$	$6k$	$12k$	$20k$	$30k$

Thus $70k = 1 \Rightarrow k = \frac{1}{70}$.

Now we can fill the probabilities into the table and work out the expected mean.

x	2	3	4	5	6
$P(X = x)$	$\frac{2}{70}$	$\frac{6}{70}$	$\frac{12}{70}$	$\frac{20}{70}$	$\frac{30}{70}$

$$E(X) = 2 \times \frac{2}{70} + 3 \times \frac{6}{70} + 4 \times \frac{12}{70} + 5 \times \frac{20}{70} + 6 \times \frac{30}{70} = \frac{350}{70} = 5$$

The following table shows the probability distribution of a discrete random variable X:

x	–1	0	1	2	3
$P(X = x)$	0.2	$10k^2$	0	0.4	$3k$

(a) Find the value of k

(b) Find the expected value of X.

(a) $10k^2 + 3k + 0.6 = 1 \Rightarrow k = 0.1$ (GDC)

(b) $E(X) = -0.2 + 0 + 0.8 + 0.9 = 1.5$

The quadratic could have been solved without a GDC. Multiply through by 10 (to make all the coefficients integers), then divide by 2 to simplify. Then factorise.

Games of chance: Let's play a game. You throw two dice. If you get a 9 or 11, I'll give you $3; if you get a double, I'll give you $2. The catch is, you must pay me $1 to play. Is it worth it? We can draw up a table of probabilities (see page 67 for how to deal with totals of two dice).

The expected mean is $\frac{6}{36} \times 3 + \frac{6}{36} \times 2 + \frac{24}{36} \times 0 = \frac{30}{36}$. Thus, on average, you can expect to win under $1 per game, so you will lose out in the long run – and you will decline my offer to play. (Moral: you can't make money out of IB Mathematics students!) You could alternatively include the $1 in the table by making the outcomes $2, $1 and –$1. This would make the expected mean $-\frac{6}{36}$.

Event	Prob.	Outcome
9 or 11	6/36	$3
Double	6/36	$2
Other	24/36	$0

4.11 The Binomial Distribution

The binomial probability distribution is a special case of a discrete distribution. You can use it when:

- there are a fixed number of "trials";
- each trial has only two possible outcomes, "success" and "failure";
- the results of each trial are independent of each other;
- the probability of success remains the same.

> You will be expected to use a calculator for binomial probabilities, and understand the difference between probability and cumulative probability.

For example, my young child wakes me up 1 night in 4. I want to find the probability that I will be woken up 3 nights out of 10.

- The number of trials, n, is 10.
- The probability of "success" (ie being woken up!) is 0.25
- We therefore say that the distribution is $X \sim B(10, 0.25)$

The calculation has three parts to it:

The number of possible arrangements of 3 nights in 10	*The probability of being woken up 3 times*	*The probability of not being woken up 7 times*

$$^{10}C_3 \times 0.25^3 \times 0.75^7 = 0.250$$

Thus there are always three parts to a binomial probability calculation **except** when you are at either end of the distribution. In which case: P(woken up all 10 nights) = 0.25^{10}; and the probability of not being woken up at all in ten nights is 0.75^{10}.

Actually,
$^{10}C_{10} \times 0.25^{10} \times 0.75^0$

Getting the probability of success: You may simply be given the probability of success, or:

- you calculate the probability from previous experience (as in the example above);
- you calculate it from your knowledge of the situation (eg: success is getting a 2 on the spinner pictured in the margin: P = 1/3);
- the probability is the result of a calculation from a previous part of the question.

This question assumes that a prizewinner can win more than one prize. Why?

Example: 350 of the 500 pupils in a school have the letter "s" in their name. Six sports prizes are awarded at the end of term. What is the probability four of the prizewinners have an "s" in their name.

Solution: The first sentence gives us the probability of success.

P("s") = $\frac{350}{500}$ = 0.7. Therefore $X \sim B(6, 0.7)$.

P(4 successes) = 0.324

More than one outcome: Since binomial probabilities are all mutually exclusive (I cannot be woken up both 3 nights **and** 4 nights in 10), the probability of one of several outcomes occurring can be found by addition. Thus, P(I am woken up 3 or 4 nights out of 10) is:

$$^{10}C_3 \times 0.25^3 \times 0.75^7 + {}^{10}C_4 \times 0.25^4 \times 0.75^6 = 0.396.$$

Check the wording of questions carefully. It might say: "Find the probability that I have at least eight nights when I am *not* woken up." Check this also gives 0.526.

Cumulative probabilities: What is the probability of being woken up on fewer than 3 nights out of 10: that is, P(0, 1, or 2). You can add these three probabilities together or use the cumulative probability function on your calculator which gives 0.526. This enables us to answer questions such as: "Find the probability that I am awoken on at least 3 nights out of 10."

Nights awoken	0	1	2	3	4	5	6	7	8	9	10
				←			want this				→
	←				Total probability = 1					→	

On some GDCs this cumulative probability could be calculated directly.

The diagram shows that the easiest way to calculate this is to find the cumulative probability up to 2, and subtract the answer from 1. This gives 1 − 0.526 = 0.474.

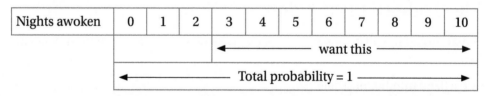

Joe is a football player. When shooting penalties, he succeeds 3 times out of every 5. In practice, he shoots 8 times. Find, to 3 significant figures, the probabilities of:

    (a) Scoring all 8 penalties.

    (b) Scoring 6 penalties out of 8.

    (c) Scoring at least 6 penalties out of 8.

$X \sim B(8, 0.6)$

    (a) P(X = 8) = 0.6^8 = 0.0168

    (b) P(X = 6) = 0.209 (GDC)

    (c) P(X ≥ 6) = 1 − P(X ≤ 5)

            = 0.315 (GDC)

It's always worth stating the distribution you are going to use – the examiner can see what you're doing, and it helps sort things out in your mind too.

In part (c) I have used the distribution functions on the GDC, but I have also shown some working to ensure method marks in case my answer is wrong.

Because there is a formula for binomial distribution probabilities, examiners sometimes like to set questions which are more algebraic in nature, such as in the following example.

The probability of an event occurring is p.

(a) Write down an expression in terms of p for the probability that the event occurs exactly 5 times out of 8.

(b) Hence find the possible values of p such that the probability of an event occurring exactly 5 times out of 8 is 0.23.

(a) $^8C_5\,p^5(1-p)^3 = 56p^5(1-p)^3$ (b) $56p^5(1-p)^3 = 0.23$ $\quad\ p = 0.513$ or 0.728 (GDC)	*(a) We have to work out for ourselves that this involves a binomial probability. This question also illustrates that, although you will often be able to work out binomial probabilities on your calculator, you do need to know the formula as well.* *(b) You might like to see my article on using the TI-84 to solve equations – see the website.*

I've included the next question here although it could well be part of a paper 2 question because it illustrates how to deal with wording which can send your mind in a spin. The key thing is to strip the wording down until it becomes possible to see the binomial probabilities required.

A machine contains a critical component. This component is replicated 10 times within the machine, and the machine works as long as at least one of the ten components is working. Each has an independent probability of failing within one year of 0.7, and all the components are replaced at the end of a year.

(a) Find the probability that all 10 fail within the year.

(b) Find the probability that the machine is in operation at the end of the year.

(c) (i) Suppose we put in n components. What is the probability that the machine is operating at the end of the year?

    (ii) Hence find the smallest number of components to install which will ensure a probability of at least 0.99 that the machine is working at the end of the year.

(a) $X \sim B(10, 0.7)$ where X = component fails $\quad\ P(X = 10) = 0.7^{10} = 0.0282$ (b) $P(\text{machine works}) = 1 - P(X = 10) = 0.9718$ (c) (i) $X \sim B(n, 0.7)$ $\qquad\ P(\text{machine works}) = 1 - 0.7^n$ (ii) $1 - 0.7^n > 0.99$ $\qquad\ 0.7^n < 0.01$ $\qquad\ n > \dfrac{\log 0.01}{\log 0.7} = 12.9$ So the smallest value of n is 13	*(a) The only issue is a semantic one – the failure of a component is a probability success!* *(b) At least 1 component working is the same as 1 – P(none are working); a familiar calculation in binomial probability questions.* *(c) Restating the distribution parameters helps to see the connection between part (c) and part (b). Note the reversal of the inequality during the working because $\log 0.7$ is a negative number. Or solve directly on the GDC.*

It is known that 1 out of 20 printed circuit boards supplied by a certain manufacturer has a fault. What is the probability that at least 1 in a batch of 10 is faulty?

Why might a binomial probability not be appropriate? Refer to the conditions on page 73 under which a binomial distribution is valid. Firstly, the events must be *independent*. The answer to the question in the notes box is 0.401. However, the assumption of independence may be wrong: the 1 in 20 is an average figure over a period of time, but perhaps if the temperature in the factory rises too much, more faulty boards are produced. Then our batch of 10, if they were all manufactured together, may have a higher incidence of faults.

Secondly, you cannot use the binomial distribution if the probabilities change. For example, there are 10 pieces of paper folded up in a box, and three have crosses marked on them. To find the probability that, when two pieces of paper are drawn out, neither has a cross, you need a tree diagram. The probabilities change each time a piece of paper is removed.

In reality, as he tires, his probability of success would probably decrease.

Expected mean: Fortunately, we do not have to go through the normal process for discrete distributions – there is a simple formula for the expected mean of a binomial distribution. Suppose Joe (who appeared a few questions back) decides to enter a marathon penalty shooting competition and goes for 400 shots. How many times would he succeed? His probability of success is 0.6, so we would expect him to succeed $0.6 \times 400 = 240$ times. Thus, if $X \sim \mathrm{B}(n, p)$, then $\mathrm{E}(X) = np$.

Remember that variance is the square of standard deviation.

Expected variance: It turns out that, not only is there a simple formula for the expected mean of a binomial distribution, there is also an equally simple one for the expected variance.

If $X \sim \mathrm{B}(n, p)$, then $\mathrm{Var}(X) = np(1 - p)$. Returning once again to Joe, the expected variance of his 400 penalty shots will be $400 \times 0.6 \times 0.4 = 96$. Thus the expected standard deviation will be $\sqrt{96} = 9.80$. What does this tell us? You should recall that we generally expect results to be within two standard deviations of the mean. In this case, with a mean of 240, this gives a likely range of about 221 to 259. If Joe scored, say, 270 penalties out of 400, we might need to question the accuracy of the 3 out of 5 figure quoted in the original question. He could be better than we thought!

In the next example we see again how a binomial distribution question leads to a bit of algebra.

Example: A binomial $X \sim (n, p)$ distribution has mean 4 and variance 2.4. Find the values of n and p.

Solution: When you have to find two unknowns, the chances are you will end up with simultaneous equations. These will arise from the formulae for the mean and the variance.

$$np = 4,$$

$$np(1 - p) = 2.4$$

Substitute the value of np from the first equation into the second:

$$4(1 - p) = 2.4 \Rightarrow p = 0.4$$

Substitute this value of p into the first equation:

$$n = \frac{4}{0.4} = 10$$

Binomial Distribution: Practice Exercise

1. $X \sim B(7, 0.25)$. Find $P(X = 5)$, the mean and variance of X.

2. $X \sim B(12, 0.8)$. Find $P(X = 10)$, $P(X > 8)$ and $P(X$ is less than 7).

3. Which is more likely: (a) $X \sim B(10, 0.15)$, $P(X = 3)$

   (b) $X \sim B(12, 0.12)$, $P(X = 3)$?

4. A coin is thrown 50 times. X represents the number of heads. What would be a likely range of values for X?

5. I work 5 days a week, and I'm late home from work about once every ten days. My partner gets cross if I'm late home more than once in a week, and I then buy them a present. How many weeks in a year would I expect to have to buy a present?

4.12 The Normal Distribution

The Normal Distribution is used to model many commonly occurring frequency distributions, eg: the heights of trees, weights of people. The curve has the following properties:

- It is symmetrical about the mean value, μ.

- The median is the same as the mean.

- The curve approaches the x-axis asymptotically (although this is not true for the majority of distributions the curve is modelling).

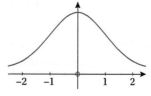

The curve (shown in the diagram) is called the *standard* normal distribution: its mean is 0, its standard deviation is 1 and the area under the curve is 1.

Standardised value: The basis of all normal distribution calculations is the *standardised value* which is the number of standard deviations that the actual value lies above or below the mean. Thus, if a group of people have a mean height 170 cm with standard deviation 10 cm, and a mean weight of 65 kg with standard deviation 5 kg, then the probability that a person chosen at random is less than 180 cm high is exactly the same as the probability of weighing less than 70 kg; both values are one standard deviation above the mean.

For a normal distribution with mean μ and standard deviation σ the formula for the standardised value is:

$$Z = \frac{x - \mu}{\sigma}$$

Simple normal probability calculations: Basic probabilities can be calculated on your GDC by entering four values: lower bound, upper bound, mean, standard deviation. In questions where there is no lower or upper bound, you can either use values such as -1×10^{99} and 1×10^{99}, or just any values much smaller or larger than those in the question.

When finding answers on your GDC you need to show some working. I suggest a shaded diagram will demonstrate to the examiner that you understand what is happening.

> Use your GDC to show that $P(-1 \leq Z \leq 1)$ is about 68%. In other words, about two thirds of all values are within one standard deviation of the mean.

> For example, if $\mu = 35$ and $\sigma = 3$, and we need to find $P(X > 40)$, then an upper bound of 100 is easily big enough.

Example: A group of people are asked to carry out a simple task. The length of time taken, in minutes, follows a normal distribution where the mean is 3.2 and standard deviation is 0.6.

(a) If a member of the group is chosen at random, find:

   (i) P(she takes between 2.5 and 3 minutes)

   (ii) P(she takes more than 3 minutes)

> This would be written as:
> $X \sim N(3.2, 0.6^2)$

Solution: (a) (i) On your GDC, enter the values for the lower and upper bounds, the mean and the SD.

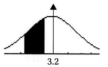

$$P(2.5 \leq X \leq 3) = 0.248$$

(ii) Now enter 3 for the lower bound, and a number such as 100 for the upper bound.

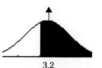

$$P(X > 3) = 0.631$$

You can also use the inverse normal function on the GDC to reverse the process. The inverse will give you the Z value associated with a particular probability, and hence the X value.

Carrying on with the previous question:

(b) The fastest 10% of the group are then selected to perform a more advanced task. What was the slowest time required to be selected?

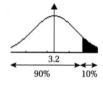

Solution: The inverse function can be used only from the left hand end of the distribution. Thus, to find the lowest value for the top 10%, we must find the highest value of the bottom 90%. Using the GDC directly we find that the slowest time was 3.97 minutes.

However, it may be advisable to show some working. Use the inverse function with $\mu = 0$, $\sigma = 1$ and area = 0.9 to give $Z = 1.28$. Then:

$$Z = \frac{X - \mu}{\sigma}, \text{ so } 1.28 = \frac{X - 3.2}{0.6}$$

Thus $X = 3.2 + 1.28 \times 0.6 = 3.97$ minutes.

> This is probably more working than you need to show in the exam – I've just included it to explain what's going on!

The next example illustrates why you must be careful using normal distribution calculations when the required answer is an integer.

Example: In a certain exam, 12% of candidates were ungraded. If the mean mark was 52 and the standard deviation was 13, and the marks were normally distributed what is the highest mark which a candidate could obtain and not gain a grade, assuming marks are integers?

Solution: Using the inverse normal function on the GDC, we find that the bottom 12% of candidates scored up to 36.7 marks. Now, 36.7 rounds to 37 – but a candidate scoring 37 would have been graded. So the highest possible mark an ungraded candidate scored is 36.

Normal Distribution: Practice Exercise

Answers

1. (a) 0.612 (b) 0.329

2. 0.48

3. 0.230

4. 78

1. For a normal distribution with mean 25 and standard deviation 3.5, find (a) P($X < 26$), (b) P($24 < X < 27$)

2. The mean of a normal distribution is 1.7, and we are given that P($X < 1.85$) = 0.74. Without using a GDC, find P($1.55 < X < 1.85$). *I suggest drawing a diagram.*

3. Calculate the standard deviation of the distribution in the previous question.

4. A set of exam results X is distributed normally with mean 65 and standard deviation 12. Where should the grade boundary be set such that no more than the top 15% of students gain an A grade in the exam?

μ and σ both unknown: A common situation in normal distribution questions is where you are asked to calculate the mean and standard deviation having been given two ranges and their associated probabilities. For example, you are given that the weights of an apple crop are distributed normally, and that:

- 25% of the apples weigh less than 120 g
- 15% of the apples weight more than 150 g

By using the inverse normal function, we can find the relevant Z values, and pair these with the X values (see diagram).

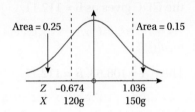

We can then substitute into the standardisation formula to form a pair of simultaneous equations:

$$-0.674 = \frac{120 - \mu}{\sigma} \text{ and } 1.036 = \frac{150 - \mu}{\sigma}$$

Solve by multiplying both sides by σ, then subtracting to eliminate μ. The solutions are: $\mu = 131.8$g, $\sigma = 17.5$g. It's a good idea to check the answer by seeing if this gives 25% of apples < 120g.

The following is a section B style question for which I have shown all the working – I think it illustrates many of the strategies you need to answer longer normal distribution questions.

> A machine is set to produce bags of salt, whose weights are distributed normally, with a mean of 110 g. If the weight of a bag of salt is less than 108 g, the bag is rejected. With these settings, 4% of the bags are rejected. The settings of the machine are altered and it is found that 7% of the bags are rejected.

*Note that you will **always** be told if a distribution is normal.*

(a) (i) If the mean has not changed, find the new SD, correct to 3 decimal places.

What has happened is that the alteration to the machine has made it less accurate; the weights are more spread out, so more fall below 108 g. The calculator tells us that an area of 0.07 is equivalent to a standardised value of −1.4758 (use 4DP to get an accurate answer to 3DP).

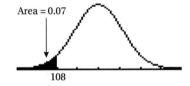

This can now be put into the standardising formula – a pivotal hinge between the calculations and the graph:

$$-1.4758 = \frac{108 - 110}{\sigma} \Rightarrow \sigma = 1.355$$

So, new standard deviation = 1.355 g

(ii) Find the value, correct to 2 decimal places, at which the mean should be set so that only 4% of the bags are rejected.

So now, accepting that we cannot improve the spread of results, we are going to increase the mean slightly (by putting more salt in each bag) and thus reduce the rejection rate. We still reject bags below 108 g.

An area of 0.04 is equivalent to $Z = -1.751$.

$$-1.751 = \frac{108 - \mu}{1.355} \Rightarrow \mu = 110.37$$

Thus, new mean = 110.37 g

The increase to the mean is small: you can see why we need to work to high accuracy.

(b) With the new settings from part (a), it is found that 80% of the bags of salt have a weight which lies between A g and B g, where A and B are symmetric about the mean. Find the values of A and B, giving your answers correct to two decimal places.

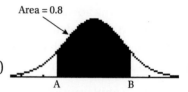

Look at the diagram. If the shaded area is 80%, then 40% is above the mean. So the total area up to B must be 90% (50 + 40).

With area = 0.9 and the mean and SD as in part (a) the GDC gives us B = 112.11.

We can then use symmetry to find A (because it is the same distance the other side of the mean).

Thus $A = 108.63, B = 112.11$

Links to other probability techniques: Probability questions do not necessarily fall into neat categories – here is a tree diagram question, there is a binomial distribution question, and that one is a normal probability question. Quite often, a question begins by asking you to calculate a probability from, say, a normal distribution, but then you might need to use that probability in a binomial distribution; you do need to recognise just what you are being asked.

Example: 40 players regularly train with the Griffins basketball squad. Their heights are normally distributed with mean 193 cm and standard deviation 4.8 cm.

    (a) Find the probability that a member of the squad is taller than 196 cm.

    (b) A team of 5 is chosen for a match. What is the probability that at least 3 of them are taller than 196cm?

Solution: (a) Using a straightforward normal distribution calculation on the GDC, we find that $P(X > 196) = 0.266$.

    (b) At least 3 out of 5? This is a binomial probability question with $Y \sim B(5, 0.266)$. In other words, the normal probability we have just calculated is the "success" probability for the binomial.

$$P(Y \geq 3) = 1 - P(Y \leq 2) = 1 - 0.879 = 0.121$$

Statistics and Probability: Long Answer Questions

Starting on the next page is a selection of Section B style exam questions related to Statistics and Probability. The answers are given here, but full workings may be found on the website.

1. A group of 100 students in a school are asked about whether they study History or Biology. 10 study neither, 60 study Biology, 72 study History.

    (a) n students take both subjects.

        (i) Show that $n = 42$.

        (ii) Write down the number of students who only study Biology.

    (b) One student is selected at random.

        (i) Find the probability that the student studies only one of the two subjects.

        (ii) Given that the student only studies one subject, find the probability that he studies History.

    (c) Let A be the event that a student studies History, and B be the event that a student studies Biology.

        (i) Explain why A and B are not mutually exclusive.

        (ii) Show that A and B are not independent.

    (d) There are 380 girls and 420 boys in the school. An opinion poll is to be carried out using a sample of 40 students.

        (i) Why would a quota sample not give reliable results?

        (ii) How many boys and how many girls would be surveyed if a stratified sample were to be set up?

    _____

Answers:

    (a) (ii) 18

    (b) (i) $\frac{48}{100}$ (ii) $\frac{30}{48}$

    (c) (i) $A \cap B \neq \varnothing$ or "Some students study both subjects"

        (ii) $P(A) \times P(B) = 0.6 \times 0.72 = 0.432.$ $P(A \text{ and } B) = 0.42.$ $0.432 \neq 0.42$

    (d) (i) Quota sampling does not produce a random sample.

        (ii) 19 girls and 21 boys.

2. A sample of 200 leaves is taken from a tree and their lengths, l cm are measured. The results are shown in the frequency table below.

Length	$0 < l \leq 1$	$1 < l \leq 2$	$2 < l \leq 3$	$3 < l \leq 4.5$	$4.5 < l \leq 6$	$6 < l \leq 8$	$8 < l \leq 10$
Frequency	30	38	52	35	25	13	7

(a) Calculate estimates for the mean and standard deviation of the lengths.

(b) (i) Draw a cumulative frequency diagram for the data using scales of 1 cm for 1 cm of length l on the horizontal axis, and 1 cm for 25 on the vertical axis.

 (ii) Estimate the median and the interquartile range from the graph.

 (iii) Use your answers to (ii) to show that a leaf measuring 8.5 cm is an outlier. Do you consider this could be an error of measurement?

(c) (i) Write down the probability that a leaf measures more than 5 cm.

 (ii) Given that a leaf measures more than 5 cm, find the probability that it measures more than 8 cm.

_____

Answers:

(a) Mean = 3.09 cm, SD = 2.11 cm

(b) (ii) Median = 2.62 IQR = 4.29 – 1.53 = 2.76

 (iii) Median + 1.5 × IQR = 6.76 cm ∴ 8.5 cm is an outlier. Probably not an error.

(c) (i) 0.185 (ii) 0.189

3. 3 playing cards are selected at random and placed in a box; the process is then repeated with 3 more numbers placed in a second box. The two boxes are found to contain the following cards:

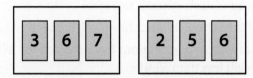

Two cards are drawn at random, one from each box.

(a) Create a list of the nine possible pairs of numbers, showing the total T in each case.

(b) Given that the selection of all pairs is equally likely, find the probability of each value of T.

(c) Find the expected value of T.

(d) George plays a game where he wins $10 if the total is less than 10, but loses $5 if the total is more than 10. What is the expected value of his winnings?

(e) How many games would George have to play before he his expected winnings were more than $45?

_____

Answers:

(a)

Pair	3,2	3,5	3,6	6,2	6,5	6,6	7,2	7,5	7,6
T	5	8	9	8	11	12	9	12	13

(b)

t	5	8	9	11	12	13
$P(T{=}t)$	$\frac{1}{9}$	$\frac{2}{9}$	$\frac{2}{9}$	$\frac{1}{9}$	$\frac{2}{9}$	$\frac{1}{9}$

(c) 9.67

(d) $3.33

(e) 14

4. It is known that a group of schoolchildren have weights which are normally distributed with a mean of 58.8 kg and standard deviation 2.28 kg.

   (a) John believes that those children whose weights lie within 10% either side of the mean all have weights within 1 kg of each other. Is he right?

   (b) Find what percentage of the schoolchildren have weights between 55.6 and 61 kg.

   (c) A group of 10 children are chosen at random from the school. What is the probability that at least 2 of them weigh less than 55.6 kg.

   (d) 60% of the school pupils are girls, and 10% of the girls weigh over 61 kg.

      (i) Complete the following table of outcomes.

	Boys	Girls	Totals
<61			
>61			17%
Totals		60%	100%

      (ii) What is the probability that a pupil chosen at random is a boy given that the pupil's weight is less than 61 kg?

Answers:

   (a) No – they lie within 1.16 kg of each other.

   (b) 75.3%

   (c) 0.188

   (d) (ii) 0.349

5. A test has five questions. To pass the test, at least three of the questions must be answered correctly.

   The probability that Sammy answers a question correctly is $\frac{1}{4}$. If X is the number of questions that Sammy answers correctly,

   (a) (i) Find $E(X)$ and $Var(X)$.

   (ii) Find the probability that Sammy passes the test.

   Martha also takes the test. Let Y be the number of questions that Martha answers correctly. The following table is the probability distribution for Y.

y	0	1	2	3	4	5
$P(Y=y)$	0.34	0.49	$p-2q$	$p-2q$	$p-3q$	0.01

   (b) (i) Show that $3p - 7q = 0.16$

   (ii) Given that $E(Y) = 1$ find p and q.

   (c) Find who is more likely to pass the test.

   _____

   Answers:

   (a) (i) 1.25, 0.9375

   (ii) 0.104

   (b) (ii) $p = 0.1$, $q = 0.02$

   (c) Martha

Chapter 5: CALCULUS

5.1 Differentiation – The Basics

The *gradient* of a graph at a point represents the rate of change of the function – so differentiation gives us the gradient of a graph at any point.

Suppose we know that the rate of inflation is 3%. This fact is useful, but would be more useful if we knew how it was changing. If its rate of change is down 0.1%/month, we can make a guess at the rate of inflation in 6 months' time. Similarly, it is useful to know we are 100 km from our destination, even more useful if we know our rate of change of distance (ie speed) is 60 kmh⁻¹. The process of finding a "rate of change function" for a given function is called differentiation. You need to know the rules for differentiating different types of function, the notation required, and the applications of differentiation.

Don't confuse:

$f'(x)$ Differentiated function

$f^{-1}(x)$ Inverse function

Notation: When you differentiate a function, the new function (the gradient function) is called the *derived* function (or *derivative*). If the original function is $f(x)$, the derived function is written as $f'(x)$. Alternatively, if the function is written in the form $y = f(x)$, the derived function is denoted by $\dfrac{dy}{dx}$.

Differentiating different types of function: You need to be able to differentiate various types of function (see table). If any functions are added or subtracted they can be differentiated independently. That is, $f(x) \pm g(x)$ differentiated is $f'(x) \pm g'(x)$.

This will not work for multiplication or division (eg to differentiate $(x+1)(x-2)$ you must first multiply out the brackets).

If a function is multiplied or divided by a *constant*, however, the constant just sits there: eg $2x^3$ differentiated is $2 \times 3x^2 = 6x^2$.

Also remember that functions of the form kx differentiate to give k, and that constants (which have a zero rate of change) differentiate to give 0.

$f(x)$	$f'(x)$
x^n	nx^{n-1}
$\sin x$	$\cos x$
$\cos x$	$-\sin x$
$\tan x$	$\sec^2 x$
e^x	e^x
$\ln(x)$	$\dfrac{1}{x}$
$x^2 - 3x$	$2x - 3$
$x^3 - 4$	$3x^2$
$2x(x-1)$	$4x - 2$

Differentiating x^n: x^n differentiates to give nx^{n-1} for all $n \in \mathbb{R}$. This allows us to differentiate reciprocal and root functions. First, remember to write these functions as powers and with x in the numerator.

Examples are:

$f(x)$	$f(x)$ rewritten	$f'(x)$	$f'(x)$ simplified
$\sqrt{x}$	$x^{\frac{1}{2}}$	$\frac{1}{2}x^{-\frac{1}{2}}$	$\dfrac{1}{2\sqrt{x}}$
$\dfrac{4}{x^2}$	$4x^{-2}$	$-8x^{-3}$	$\dfrac{-8}{x^3}$
$x\sqrt{x}$	$x^{\frac{3}{2}}$	$\frac{3}{2}x^{\frac{1}{2}}$	$\dfrac{3\sqrt{x}}{2}$
$\dfrac{2}{\sqrt{x}}$	$2x^{-\frac{1}{2}}$	$-\frac{1}{2}\times 2x^{-\frac{3}{2}}$	$-\dfrac{1}{x^{\frac{3}{2}}}$

Differentiating $\sin x$, $\cos x$ and $\tan x$: x must be in radians for these differentiations to give correct results. eg: What is the gradient of the graph of $y = x + \sin x$ when $x = 1$? $\dfrac{dy}{dx} = 1 + \cos x$ so when $x = 1$, the gradient is $1 + \cos 1 = 1.54$. With the calculator set in degrees, you would get 1.9998.

> Make sure you know how to use your GDC to find the gradient of a curve at a point.

Apart from adding or subtracting functions, we must use certain rules for differentiating functions when they are combined in different ways.

5.2 The Chain Rule

The Chain Rule is used to differentiate composite functions. Consider the function $y = (4x + 3)^2$. If we write the "inner function" (ie $4x + 3$) as a single letter u, then the function becomes $y = u^2$. The chain rule shows us how the rates of change of *three* variables (as opposed to two) are connected:

$$\frac{dy}{dx} = \frac{dy}{du} \times \frac{du}{dx}$$

We can then use the chain rule like this:

I've written a fuller explanation of the Chain Rule on the website.

$$u = 4x + 3 \qquad\qquad \frac{du}{dx} = 4$$

$$y = u^2 \qquad\qquad \frac{dy}{du} = 2u$$

$$\frac{dy}{dx} = \frac{dy}{du} \times \frac{du}{dx} = 2u \times 4 = 8u = 8(4x + 3)$$

An alternative, informal, method is to proceed as follows:

- Take the "inner function" (in brackets) and differentiate it: $\quad 4$
- Work out the "outer function" differentiated: $\quad (\ldots)^2 \rightarrow \ 2(\ldots)$
- Multiply the two together: $\quad 8(\ldots)$
- Fill in the brackets: $\quad 8(4x + 3)$

Here are more examples using the informal method:

$f(x) = \cos(2x - 4)$

Inner function is $2x - 4$

Differentiate inner $\rightarrow$ 2

Differentiate $\cos(...) \rightarrow -\sin(...)$

Multiply $-2\sin(...)$

Result: $f'(x) = -2\sin(2x - 4)$

$f(x) = \ln(1 + x^2)$

Inner function is $1 + x^2$

Differentiate inner $\rightarrow 2x$

Differentiate $\ln(...) = \dfrac{1}{(...)}$

Multiply $2x \times \dfrac{1}{(...)}$

Result: $f'(x) = \dfrac{2x}{(1 + x^2)}$

$f(x) = \sqrt{1 - 5x} = (1 - 5x)^{\frac{1}{2}}$

Inner function is $1 - 5x$

Differentiate inner $\rightarrow -5$

Differentiate $(...)^{\frac{1}{2}} \rightarrow \frac{1}{2}(...)^{-\frac{1}{2}}$

Multiply $-\frac{5}{2}(...)^{-\frac{1}{2}}$

Result: $f'(x) = -\frac{5}{2}(1 - 5x)^{-\frac{1}{2}}$

$f(x) = e^{x^3} = e^{(x^3)}$

Inner function is x^3

Differentiate inner $\rightarrow 3x^2$

Differentiate $e^{(...)} \rightarrow e^{(...)}$

Multiply $3x^2 \times e^{(...)}$

Result: $f'(x) = 3x^2(e^{x^3})$

Chain Rule: Practice Exercise

Answers

1. (a) $2\cos 2x$

 (b) $\dfrac{2}{2x + 3}$

 (c) $\dfrac{-3}{x^2}\left(1 + \dfrac{1}{x}\right)^2$

 (d) $-6\sin x \cos x$

2. $-e^{-2} + 1, x = 0$

3. $a = 2$ or 6

1. Differentiate the following functions:

    (a) $\sin 2x$

    (b) $\ln(2x + 3)$

    (c) $\left(1 + \dfrac{1}{x}\right)^3$

    (d) $3\cos^2 x$

2. Given that $f(x) = e^{-x} + x$, find $f'(2)$ and the value of x for which $f'(x) = 0$.

3. Given that $f(x) = \dfrac{1}{x^2 - a}$ and $f'(2) = -1$, find the possible values of a.

Let $f(x) = \cos x$ and $g(x) = 2x^2$. Find expressions for $(g \circ f)(x)$ and $(f \circ g)'(x)$.

(a) $(g \circ f)(x) = g(\cos x) = 2(\cos x)^2 = 2\cos^2 x$

(b) $(f \circ g)(x) = f(2x^2) = \cos(2x^2)$

$u = 2x^2 \qquad \dfrac{du}{dx} = 4x$

$y = \cos u \qquad \dfrac{dy}{du} = -\sin u$

$\dfrac{dy}{dx} = \dfrac{dy}{du} \times \dfrac{du}{dx} = -4x \sin u = -4x \sin(2x^2)$

Calculus questions often involve maths from any of the other areas of the syllabus – in this case we have to find a composite function and then differentiate it.

We can identify it as a chain rule differentiation because one function is contained within a second function.

5.3 Product and Quotient Rules

When you have to differentiate two functions multiplied together you must use the *product rule*; and when two functions are divided, you must use the *quotient rule*. If the two functions are $u(x)$ and $v(x)$ – normally shortened to u and v – then the rules are:

- Product Rule: $\frac{d}{dx}(uv) = u\frac{dv}{dx} + v\frac{du}{dx}$

- Quotient Rule: $\frac{d}{dx}\left(\frac{u}{v}\right) = \frac{v\frac{du}{dx} - u\frac{dv}{dx}}{v^2}$

It may be helpful to think of the rules more informally as:

Product Rule:

(1st fn × 2nd fn differentiated) + (2nd fn × 1st fn differentiated)

Quotient Rule:

$$\frac{(\text{bottom} \times \text{top differentiated}) - (\text{top} \times \text{bottom differentiated})}{(\text{bottom line squared})}$$

Note the plus sign in the product rule and the minus sign in the quotient rule. Also remember that, because of the minus sign, the order is important in the quotient rule.

When you are asked to do these more complicated differentiations, you can either write down every step in the formulae (safe but time-consuming) or you can do some of it in your head (faster, but you can go wrong). Here is an example of full working:

Example: Differentiate $y = x^2 \sin x$

Solution: $u = x^2$ $\frac{du}{dx} = 2x$

$v = \sin x$ $\frac{dv}{dx} = \cos x$

$\frac{dy}{dx} = u\frac{dv}{dx} + v\frac{du}{dx} = x^2 \cos x + 2x \sin x$

It is possible that either (or both, if you are unlucky) of u and v are composite functions, in which case you will have to use the chain rule as well.

Example: Differentiate $f(x) = \frac{\sin(2x+3)}{x^2}$

Solution: $u = \sin(2x+3)$ $\frac{du}{dx} = 2\cos(2x+3)$

$v = x^2$ $\frac{dv}{dx} = 2x$

$\frac{dy}{dx} = \frac{v\frac{du}{dx} - u\frac{dv}{dx}}{v^2} = \frac{2x^2\cos(2x+3) - 2x\sin(2x+3)}{x^4}$

$= \frac{2x(x\cos(2x+3) - \sin(2x+3))}{x^4}$

$= \frac{2(x\cos(2x+3) - \sin(2x+3))}{x^3}$

Once you have differentiated, don't forget that the end result is, as with all differentiation, however complicated, the rate of change of the original function, the gradient of the graph at any point.

> Another quick way to remember them:
>
> Product Rule is $uv' + vu'$
>
> Quotient Rule is $\frac{vu' - uv'}{v^2}$

> Note the simplification in the last two lines. Complicated quotient rule differentiations often end up with a bit of factorisation and cancelling.

89

There is sometimes confusion when deciding whether to use the chain rule or the product rule. If x appears twice in the function, it's probably a product rule; if not, it's either a simple differentiation or it's the chain rule.

Product and Quotient Rules: Practice Exercise

1. Differentiate, simplifying where possible:

    (a) $x^3 \ln x$

    (b) $x\sqrt{x+3}$

    (c) $\sin x \cos(2x)$

    (d) $3x^2 e^x$

2. Differentiate, simplifying where possible:

    (a) $\dfrac{x+1}{2x-1}$

    (b) $\dfrac{x^2}{e^{2x}}$

    (c) $\tan x$ *(Use one of the trig identities)*

    (d) $\dfrac{4\ln x}{x^2}$

Notes on algebraic simplification: Questions such as those in the practice exercise above probably test your algebra more than anywhere else in the course. The issue arises: what counts as simplification, and what is just rearrangement?

The main point to make is that, on its own, factorisation isn't simplification. In question 1(a), the answer $x^2 + 3x^2\ln x$ is equally valid. However, factorisation can lead to further simplification, particularly in algebraic fractions. Take 2(b) as an example – here's the full working:

$$f'(x) = \frac{e^{2x} \times 2x - x^2 \times 2e^x}{(e^{2x})^2}$$

$$= \frac{2xe^{2x}(1-x)}{(e^{2x})^2}$$

$$= \frac{2x(1-x)}{e^{2x}}$$

Without the top line factorisation, the rest of the simplification could not take place. Factorisation also helps, as we shall see, when solving problems involving turning points.

The other question I am frequently asked is whether or not expressions with negative or fractional powers can be left as they are. The answer is "yes", although I prefer to get rid of them if further work (such as substituting vales for x) is going to be required. The answer I have given to 1(b) isn't the only possibility. Again, here's the working – and you'll see that we can take the working even further and write the result as a single fraction.

$$f'(x) = x \times \tfrac{1}{2}(x+3)^{-\frac{1}{2}} + (x+3)^{\frac{1}{2}} \times 1$$

$$= \frac{x}{2(x+3)^{\frac{1}{2}}} + (x+3)^{\frac{1}{2}}$$

$$= \frac{x}{2\sqrt{x+3}} + \sqrt{x+3}$$

$$= \frac{x + 2(x+3)}{2\sqrt{x+3}}$$

$$= \frac{3x+6}{2\sqrt{x+3}}$$

Any of line 1 (tidied up a bit), line 2, line 3 or line 5 would be good answers. But isn't line 5 a satisfying result compared to line 1!

5.4 Second Derivative

Notation: When a function is differentiated a second time, use the notation $\dfrac{d^2y}{dx^2}$ or $f''(x)$.

Interpretation: The first derivative gives us the gradient function, so the second derivative gives us the "rate of change of gradient" function. If, for example, $f''(3) = 2$, this means that when $x = 3$, the gradient of the graph is increasing at a rate of 2 (for every increase in x of 1). It does not necessarily mean that the gradient itself is positive – only that it is increasing. This tells us about the shape of the curve. The diagram below shows what happens for various values of the first and second derivatives and covers every possible point on any curve.

Note the following:

- For a point of inflexion to occur $f''(x) = 0$, but the gradient at a point of inflexion is not necessarily 0.
- A point where $f''(x) = 0$ is not necessarily a point of inflexion. For example, $y = x^4$ has a *minimum* when $f''(x) = 0$.
- The sign of the second derivative at a turning point identifies the nature of the point: a maximum if $f''(x) < 0$, a minimum if $f''(x) > 0$. But you can also use "sign diagrams" (see the Applications of Differentiation section on page 94).

	$\dfrac{dy}{dx} < 0$	$\dfrac{dy}{dx} = 0$	$\dfrac{dy}{dx} > 0$
$\dfrac{d^2y}{dx^2} < 0$		MAXIMUM	
$\dfrac{d^2y}{dx^2} = 0$		POINTS OF INFLEXION	
$\dfrac{d^2y}{dx^2} > 0$		MINIMUM	

Imagine the graph is a road, and you are driving from left to right.

Right hand bends represent a decreasing gradient, so the second derivative < 0. Left hand bends represent an increasing gradient, so the second derivative > 0.

Points of inflexion occur whenever the steering wheel is momentarily straight: second derivative = 0 but this *doesn't* have to be when the gradient of the graph is 0.

Note that the parts of curves in the top row are known as "concave down" and those in the bottom row as "concave up."

Use the product rule to find and identify the stationary point on the graph of $f(x) = xe^{-x}$.		

$u = x$ $\qquad u' = 1$	We are told to use the product rule, so we can't use the GDC to find the stationary point (although if it is Paper 2 we can use the GDC to check our answer).
$v = e^{-x}$ $\qquad v' = -e^x$	
$\qquad f'(x) = uv' + vu'$	
$\qquad\qquad = -xe^{-x} + e^{-x}$	
For a stationary point $f'(x) = 0$	Note how factorisation leads straight to the answer. Also remember that exponential functions cannot ever equal zero.
$\qquad -xe^{-x} + e^{-x} = 0$	
$\qquad e^{-x}(1 - x) = 0$	
$\qquad\qquad x = 1$	To find the second derivative, note that the first term in $f'(x)$ is exactly the same as $f(x)$, with a minus sign. We've already differentiated that! Also note that we don't necessarily have to find the value of $f''(x)$ – just its sign.
When $x = 1$, $y = 1 \times e^{-1} = e^{-1}$	
So the stationary point is $(1, e^{-1})$ or $\left(1, \frac{1}{e}\right)$	
$\qquad f''(x) = -(-xe^{-x} + e^{-x}) - e^{-x} = xe^{-x} - 2e^{-x}$	
When $x = 1$, $f''(x) = 1e^{-1} - 2e^{-1} < 0$	
So the stationary point is a maximum.	

5.5 Graphical Behaviour of Functions

If we are shown the graph of a function we can tell where the values of $f(x)$, $f'(x)$, and $f''(x)$ are increasing, decreasing or zero. Slightly harder, if we are given the graph of $f'(x)$ we can do the same thing. The key point is that we do not need to know what the actual function is. For example, suppose this sketch is part of the graph of $f'(x)$:

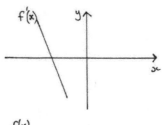

$f'(x)$ tells us the *values* of the gradient of $f(x)$. So when $f'(x) > 0$ (ie its graph is above the x-axis) the graph of the function has positive gradients – it is an *increasing* function. When $f'(x) = 0$ we've got a stationary point; and then the values of the gradient go negative, so we have a *decreasing* function.

What we don't know are the actual values of the function, only its behaviour. So the next sketch shows what the graph of the function is doing, but at this stage I can't put any axes in.

A couple of examples should cover the various techniques you will need to answer exam questions.

Example: The following diagram shows a part of the graph of $y = f(x)$.

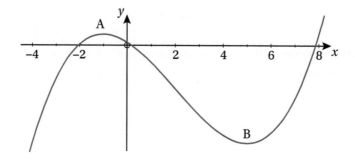

The graph has a local maximum at A, where $x = -1$, and a local minimum at B, where $x = 5$.

(a) For what values of x is f a decreasing function?

(b) Sketch the graph of $f'(x)$.

(c) Write down the following in order from least to greatest:

$f(0), f'(5), f''(-1)$.

Solution: (a) $-1 < x < 5$. (It is **not** decreasing at the turning points themselves).

(b) To draw the sketch, let's consider the values of $f'(x)$. Up to the point A, f is an increasing function, so the values of f' are positive – but getting less so. At A the gradient is 0, and then it is negative until B. Between A and B there is a point of inflexion; at this point the gradient reaches its largest negative value. After B the gradient is positive again, and increasing. This leads to the following sketch:

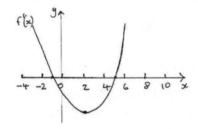

> I did this sketch in pen so it would reproduce properly. But I suggest you *always* use pencil for your diagrams and graphs. So much easier to make corrections.

How do I know it's a curve? Because if it were two straight lines this would lead to a sharp point at $x = 2$, and this can't happen.

(c) $f(0)$ is positive, from original graph.

$f'(5) = 0$ because it's a stationary point

$f''(-1)$ is negative, because it's a maximum point

So, in increasing order, $f''(0), f'(5), f(0)$

Now have a look at this graph which shows the derived function, $f'(x)$, of a function which has a domain $-3 \le x \le 3$.

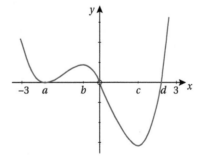

The graph of $f'(x)$ has minimum points when $x = a$ and when $x = c$, and a maximum point when $x = b$. It has zeroes when $x = a$ and $x = d$.

What can we deduce about the function?

- When is the function decreasing? This occurs whenever the gradient is negative, so when the graph of f' is below the axis. Answer: $0 < x < d$

- Where does the graph of $f(x)$ have a minimum? This will occur when the gradient is 0, so it could be at $x = a$, $x = 0$, or $x = d$. But a minimum has positive gradient to the left and negative gradient to the right; looking at the values of $f'(x)$ we can see that the only point which fits the criteria is where $x = 0$.

- Points of inflexion occur when $f''(x) = 0$, so at stationary points on $f'(x)$. At the same time, the gradient must have the same sign either side of the point of inflexion (ie both positive or both negative). Thus all of $x = a$, $x = b$, and $x = c$ are points of inflexion on the graph of $f(x)$.

5.6 Applications of Differentiation

Equations of tangents and normals: A tangent to a graph has the same gradient as at the point on the graph where the tangent touches, and the normal is perpendicular to the tangent. Knowing this, and the point itself, we can find the equations of the tangent and the normal. Remember that when you differentiate a function you get the *gradient function*.

Example: Find the equation of the tangent to $y = 2x^2 - 4x + 3$ at the point where $x = 2$.

Remembering that the gradients of perpendicular lines multiply to give -1, show that the equation of the normal is $x + 4y = 14$

Solution: $\dfrac{dy}{dx} = 4x - 4$ ∴ When $x = 2$, $\dfrac{dy}{dx} = 4$

When $x = 2$, $y = 3$

$$y - y_1 = m(x - x_1)$$

$$y - 3 = 4(x - 2)$$

$$y = 4x - 5$$

Tangents and Normals: Practice Exercise

Answers

1. $y = x - 1$
2. $(2, 11)$
3. $y = 9x + 16$
4. $k = -\dfrac{1}{95}$

(These questions should be tried both with and without GDC).

1. Find the equation of the tangent to $y = x^2 \ln x$ where $x = 1$

2. T is the tangent to the curve $y = x^2 + 6x - 4$ at $(1, 3)$ and N is the normal to the curve $y = x^2 - 6x + 18$ at $(4, 10)$. Find the point of intersection of T and N.

3. Find the equation of the tangent to the curve $y = x^3 - 3x$ which is parallel to the tangent at the point $(2, 2)$.

 4. Consider $f(x) = 2kx^3 + \dfrac{k}{x}$. The gradient of the normal line to $f(x)$ at $x = 2$ equals 4. Find the value of k.

Maximum and minimum points: The point where a graph "turns round" can be very significant. For example, if the graph shows values of profit against selling price for a particular product, the maximum shows the selling price which leads to maximum profit.

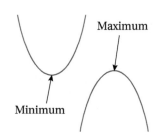

Maximum

Minimum

- To find a maximum or minimum, differentiate the function then find where the gradient is 0.

- To tell which sort of point you have, use the second derivative or a sign diagram (see worked question below) if it is easier.

Find the turning point on the graph of $y = \ln(2 + x^2)$ giving coordinates as exact values. Determine whether the turning point is a maximum or a minimum.

Using the chain rule, $\dfrac{dy}{dx} = \dfrac{2x}{2 + x^2}$

For a turning point, $\dfrac{dy}{dx} = 0 \Rightarrow 2x = 0 \Rightarrow x = 0$

When $x = 0$, $y = \ln 2$ $\therefore$ Turning point is $(0, \ln 2)$

x	-1	0	1
$\dfrac{dy}{dx}$	╲	—	╱

From the sign diagram $(0, \ln 2)$ is a minimum.

When finding turning points, you will often find that you are setting an algebraic fraction to equal zero. Make the numerator zero – the denominator is irrelevant.

For the sign diagram, take a value of x either side of the turning point and work out the sign of the gradient at these points. You can usually do this without working out exact values. In this case, for example, the denominator will always be positive, so just look at the sign of 2x.

You can see from the previous worked example that it is not necessary to draw a graph to find its turning points. However, make sure you can use your calculator to find maximum and minimum values: for example, find the x-coordinates of all maximums and minimums on the graph of $f(x) = \sin(1 + \sin x)$, $0 \le x \le 6$.

Turning Points and Points of Inflexion: Practice Exercise

1. Find all the turning points, if any, on the following graphs, and identify them as maximums or minimums (try with and without GDC).

    (a) $y = x^3 + 6x^2 - 15x + 3$

    (b) $y = \dfrac{x}{\ln x}$

    (c) $y = \dfrac{x^2}{1 + x}$

    (d) $y = 3 + \dfrac{4}{x}$

2. Given $f(x) = x^2 e^x$ where $-1 \le x \le 0$:

    (a) Find $f''(x)$

    (b) Solve $f''(x) = 0$

    (c) Hence find the point of inflexion on the graph of f, and use a sign diagram to confirm it is a point of inflexion.

3. Let $f(x) = e^x(2 - x^2)$

    (a) Use the product rule to show that $f'(x) = e^x(2 - 2x - x^2)$

    (b) Write down, to 3SF, the x values of the maximum and minimum points.

    (c) Find the equation of the normal to the curve where $x = 0$.

Answers

1. (a) Max$(-5, 103)$, Min$(1, -5)$
   (b) Min(e, e)
   (c) Max$(-2, -4)$, Min$(0, 0)$
   (d) No turning points
2. (a) $e^x(x^2 + 4x + 2)$
   (b) $x = -0.586$
   (c) $(-0.586, 0.191)$
   -ve gradient both sides
3. (b) $-2.73, 0.732$
   (c) $x + 2y = 4$

Velocity and acceleration: Since velocity is rate of change of displacement, differentiating a displacement-time function will give velocity. Similarly, differentiating a velocity-time function will give acceleration (which is the rate at which velocity changes).

Let's consider the motion of a ball thrown straight up in the air and whose height h m at time t seconds is given by $h = 20t - 5t^2$, for $0 \le t \le 4$. We can find its velocity at any time t by differentiating: $v = \dfrac{dh}{dt} = 20 - 10t$.

The following table shows its height and velocity at different times:

t (seconds)	0	1	2	3	4
h (m)	0	15	20	15	0
v (m/s)	20	10	0	–10	–20

What does this tell us? Looking at the height, it appears to reach a maximum of 20 m before falling down and hitting the ground at 4 s. The initial velocity is 20 m/s; at 2 s its velocity is 0 m/s, confirming we are at maximum height, and then the velocity becomes negative, showing that it has reversed direction.

In the previous section we saw that to find a maximum or minimum we differentiate and set equal to 0. This is exactly what we have done here, the only difference being that the differentiated function actually has a physical meaning – velocity.

An interesting point is the difference between displacement and distance. At $t = 3$ s, the ball's displacement is 15 m; this is the difference between its current position and its initial position. But the distance it has travelled is $20 + 5 = 25$ m. We shall look at this again on page 101 in the integration section.

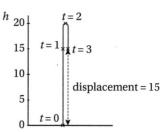

Optimisation problems: Optimisation problems boil down to this:

- Find a function relating two real-life quantities
- Find the value of the first variable which leads to a maximum or minimum (the *optimum value*) of the second variable

The second part is just the same as finding a turning point on a graph – it's often the first part which causes head scratching because it involves setting up an equation.

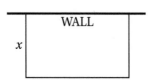

Let us suppose that a farmer has 80 m of fencing which he is going to use to enclose a rectangular sheep pen – he's going to use a stone wall as one side, and the fence to make up the other three sides of rectangle. What dimensions should the rectangle be so as to enclose the maximum area?

Let's call the width of the rectangle x. The opposite side will also be x leaving $80 - 2x$ for the length. So the area is $x(80 - 2x)$. Now it's the area we want to optimise, so:

$$A = x(80 - 2x)$$
$$= 80x - 2x^2$$
$$\frac{dA}{dx} = 80 - 4x$$

For a maximum, $80 - 4x = 0 \Rightarrow x = 20$.

So the dimensions of the rectangle are 20 m × 40 m, giving an area of 800 m². We don't need it, but I've also plotted the graph of $A = x(80 - 2x)$ to show that there is a maximum at (20, 800).

The sum of the height and the base of a triangle is 40 cm. Find an expression for its area in terms of x, its base length. Hence find its maximum area.

If x is the base, the height is $40 - x$ The area is $\frac{1}{2} \times$ base $\times$ height $= \frac{1}{2}x(40 - x)$ $\qquad = 20x - \frac{1}{2}x^2$ The area is $\frac{1}{2} \times$ base $\times$ height $= \frac{1}{2}x(40 - x)$ $\qquad = 20x - \frac{1}{2}x^2$ $\qquad \frac{dA}{dx} = 20 - x$ $\therefore$ Maximum when $20 - x = 0$, so $x = 20$ Max area $= 10 \times 20 = 200 \text{ cm}^2$	*Just remember this: whenever you see the words "minimum" or "maximum", it's likely you're going to need differentiation!*

Higher derivatives: The notations for first and second derivatives can be extended to higher derivatives. In general, the notation of the nth derivative of a function is either $\frac{d^n x}{dx^n}$ or $f^{(n)}x$.

Example: Find the first, second and third derivatives of $y = xe^x$ and hence suggest a formula for the nth derivative.

Solution: Using the product rule and factorising the results we find that:

$$\frac{dy}{dx} = (1 + x)e^x, \quad \frac{d^2y}{dx^2} = (2 + x)e^x, \quad \frac{d^3y}{dx^3} = (3 + x)e^x$$

This suggests that $\frac{d^n y}{dx^n} = (n + x)e^x$

Differentiation: Practice Exercise

1. Differentiate each of the following functions. In each case, find the equations of the tangent and the normal for the given x value.

   (a) $y = x^2 - \frac{6}{x}, x = -1$

   (b) $y = \sqrt{2x + 1}, x = 4$

   (c) $y = \sin x + \cos x, x = \frac{\pi}{2}$

   (d) $y = \frac{x^2}{x + 1}, x = 1$

2. Find the coordinates of the maximum point on the graph of $y = \frac{x}{e^x}$ giving your answer in an exact form.

3. Find the point of inflexion on the graph of $y = 3x^2 - x^3$. What is the gradient of the graph at that point?

4. Use the chain rule to differentiate $y = \sin x^2$ and $(\sin x)^2$. Use your GDC to find the value of x for which these graphs have the same gradient, $\frac{\pi}{4} \le x \le \frac{\pi}{2}$.

5. Find the dimensions of a rectangle with area 100 cm² such that the perimeter is as short as possible.

   Hint: If the length is x cm, what will the width be in terms of x? Now work out the perimeter in terms of x, and differentiate.

Answers

1. a) $2x + 6x^{-2}, y = 4x + 11$

   $y = -\frac{1}{4}x + 6\frac{3}{4}$

   b) $(2x + 1)^{-\frac{1}{2}}, 3y = x + 5$

   $y = 15 - 3x$

   c) $\cos x - \sin x$,

   $y = -x + \frac{\pi}{2} + 1$

   $y = x - \frac{\pi}{2} + 1$

   d) $\frac{x(x + 2)}{(x + 1)^2}, 4y = 3x - 1$

   $8x + 6y = 11$

2. $(1, e^{-1})$

3. $(1, 2); 3$

4. $2x \cos x^2, 2\sin x \cos x$; 1.088

5. 10 cm × 10 cm

5.7 Indefinite Integrals

Integration is sometimes called "anti-differentiation": that is, it is the reverse operation to differentiation. However, the notation is very different, and you must understand two forms – the indefinite and the definite integral.

Notation: If we just consider functions of the form ax^n, then to reverse the differentiation process we must add 1 to n then divide by the new power. For example, $4x^2$ integrated is $\frac{4}{3}x^3$. The full notation for this is: $\int 4x^2\, dx = \frac{4}{3}x^3$. The $\int$ sign means "integrate", then comes the function you want to integrate, then dx. However, the answer is not entirely correct. If you differentiate $\frac{4}{3}x^3$ you will certainly get $4x^2$, but this will also be true if you differentiate $\frac{4}{3}x^3 + 2$, $\frac{4}{3}x^3 - 1$, and so on. In other words, when we integrate, there could be a constant at the end. Since we don't know what it is, we add a 'c' which is called "the constant of integration." So we end up with $\int 4x^2\, dx = \frac{4}{3}x^3 + c$, and you must remember to add c to every indefinite integral – hence the word "indefinite."

Integrating x^n: Generally, then, $\int ax^n\, dx = \frac{ax^{n+1}}{n+1} + c$ and, as with differentiation, $n \in \mathbb{Q}$. There is one exception, and that is when integrating $\frac{1}{x}$. Since this is x^{-1}, the rule above would give $\frac{x^0}{0}$ and this is undefined. But since differentiating $\ln x$ gives $\frac{1}{x}$, it follows that $\int \frac{1}{x}\, dx = \ln|x| + c$.

> The absolute value is required so that we can deal with negative values of x.

Integrating other functions:

$f(x)$	$\int f(x)\, dx$
$\sin x$	$-\cos x$
$\cos x$	$\sin x$
e^x	e^x

Also, as with differentiation, it is true that

$$\int f(x) + g(x)\, dx = \int f(x)\, dx + \int g(x)\, dx \text{ and } \int kf(x)\, dx = k\int f(x)\, dx$$

> Note that the b in $ax + b$ isn't relevant to the process.
> For example:
> $\int \cos 3x\, dx = \frac{1}{3}\sin 3x + c$.

Integrating functions of the form $f(ax + b)$: Consider what you get when you differentiate $f(x) = \sin(2x + 3)$. The "inner function" (see Chain Rule on page 87) is $2x + 3$, and this differentiates to give 2, so overall we get $f'(x) = 2\cos(2x + 3)$. Now let's reverse the process to find $\int \cos(2x + 3)\, dx$. Since $2\cos(2x + 3)$ must integrate to give $\sin(2x + 3)$, it follows that $\int \cos(2x + 3)\, dx = \frac{1}{2}\sin(2x + 3) + c$. This leads to the general result: $\int f(ax + b)\, dx = \frac{1}{a}F(ax + b) + c$, where $F(x) = \int f(x)\, dx$. Here are some more examples:

$$\int e^{3x-1}\, dx = \frac{1}{3}e^{3x-1}$$

$$\int \frac{1}{2x-4}\, dx = \frac{1}{2}\ln(2x-4) + c$$

$$\int (3-4x)^2\, dx = -\frac{1}{4} \times \frac{1}{3}(3-4x)^3 = -\frac{1}{12}(3-4x)^3 + c$$

If there is a constant multiplying the function, just leave it sitting around while you do the integration – it plays no part in the proceedings, but might help simplify the final result. For example:

$$\int 4\sin(2x + 1)\, dx = 4 \times \left(-\frac{1}{2}\right)\cos(2x + 1) = -2\cos(2x + 1) + c$$

Reversing the chain rule: Integrating $f(ax+b)$ is a specific instance of integration by reverse chain rule. More generally, if you spot an integral which is made up of a composite function multiplied by the inner function differentiated, you can guess the solution and see what happens when you differentiate it. Putting it in words is pretty incomprehensible so perhaps a diagram will help:

$$\int 3x^2 \cos(x^3)\, dx$$

This function is this one differentiated,
so let's first try differentiating $\sin(x^3)$.

Using the chain rule, we find that $f(x) = \sin(x^3) \Rightarrow f'(x) = 3x^2 \cos(x^3)$ which is exactly what we want. So $\int 3x^2 \cos(x^3)\, dx = \sin(x^3) + c$.

Sometimes you have to adjust by multiplying by a constant. For example, let's examine $\int 4x(x^2+3)^3\, dx$. The overall function is a cubic, so will integrate to power 4. The inner function is x^2+3 and that differentiates to give $2x$; well, we've got $4x$ in front of the bracket, so a multiplier will sort that out. One way to tackle this is to try differentiating $(x^2+3)^4$, and this yields $8x(x^2+3)^3$. Comparing with the required integral, we conclude that $\int 4x(x^2+3)^3\, dx = \frac{1}{2}(x^2+3)^4 + c$.

Here are some $f(ax+b)$ and reverse chain rule examples for you to try:

(a) $\int \frac{1}{4x-3} dx$; (b) $\int e^{2x} dx$; (c) $\int 4x \sin(x^2)\, dx$; (d) $\int 9x^2 \sqrt{x^3-4}\, dx$

(e) $\int \frac{6x^2}{x^3-2} dx$ *(Try ln (x^3-2))*; (f) $\int \frac{1}{\sqrt{2x-1}} dx$; (g) $\int \cos x(\sin^3 x)\, dx$

Solving gradient function equations: In some questions we are given the gradient (ie derived) function and asked to find the original function which gave rise to it. This means we must integrate the gradient function.

For example, if $f'(x) = 3x^2 - x^3$, find $f(x)$.

So, $f(x) = \int 3x^2 - x^3\, dx = x^3 - \frac{1}{4}x^4 + c$, but we will need more information to find the value of c.

Suppose we know that $f(2) = 6$ (in other words, when $x = 2$, $y = 6$). We then substitute this into the equation to get: $6 = 8 - 4 + c$, and $c = 2$. So the function we are looking for is $f(x) = x^3 - \frac{1}{4}x^4 + 2$.

As ever, exam questions may pose the question in different ways, such as:

The graph of a function h passes through the point $\left(\frac{\pi}{6}, \sqrt{3}\right)$. Given that $h'(x) = 8 \cos 2x$, find $h(x)$. The solution is $h(x) = 4 \sin 2x - \sqrt{3}$.

> **Answers**
> (a) $\frac{1}{4}\ln(4x-3) + c$
> (b) $\frac{1}{2}e^{2x} + c$
> (c) $-2\cos(x^2) + c$
> (d) $2(x^3-4)^{\frac{3}{2}} + c$
> (e) $2\ln(x^3-2) + c$
> (f) $\sqrt{2x-1} + c$
> (g) $\frac{1}{4}\sin^4 x + c$

> Full working can be found on the website

5.8 Definite Integrals

Differentiating $f(x)$ gives us a new function from which we can determine the gradient at any point on the graph of $f(x)$. Similarly, integrating $f(x)$ results in a new function from which we can find the area under the graph. To do this we must define the vertical lines which bound the area. The x values are called the *limits* and, when included, result in a *definite* integral. The integration process is the same as before, but then follow the steps necessary to evaluate the area.

> An indefinite integral:
> $\int (x^2+2)\, dx$
> A definite integral:
> $\int_1^3 (x^2+2)\, dx$

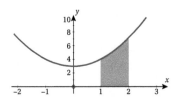

The diagram shows a shaded area bounded by the x-axis, the graph $y = x^2 + 3$, and the lines $x = 1$ and $x = 2$. The area is calculated by evaluating the definite integral $\int_1^2 x^2 + 3 \, dx$.

The procedure is:

- Integrate the function, omitting the constant of integration.
- Put the result into square brackets with the limits outside.
- Substitute the limits into the integrated function (upper limit first) and subtract the two numbers. The result is the area.

The *c* can be left out because it will always cancel out in the subtraction which follows.

Two important points:

- Definite integrals which evaluate an area **below** the x-axis will have negative values – although the area, of course, is still positive.
- Limits written right-to-left will also result in a negative value.

So, for our graph, the shaded area is calculated as follows:

▣ Your GDC can evaluate definite integrals – make sure you know how.

$$A = \int_1^2 x^2 + 3 \, dx$$

$$= \left[\tfrac{1}{3}x^3 + 3x\right]_1^2$$

$$= \left(\tfrac{1}{3} \times 2^3 + 6\right) - \left(\tfrac{1}{3} \times 1^3 + 3\right)$$

$$= \tfrac{8}{3} + 6 - \tfrac{1}{3} - 3$$

$$= \tfrac{16}{3}$$

Note how I have been careful not to take any shortcuts with the substitution and the calculation – this is particularly necessary when there are lots of minus signs flying around, as demonstrated in the next example. My motto is: you can never use too many brackets!

Example: Find the area enclosed by the x-axis, the lines $x = \frac{\pi}{2}$, $x = \pi$, and the graph of $y = 3 \sin x - 2$.

Solution: $A = \int_{\frac{\pi}{2}}^{\pi} 3 \sin x - 2 \, dx$

$$= [-3 \cos x - 2x]_{\frac{\pi}{2}}^{\pi}$$

$$= (-3 \cos \pi - 2 \times \pi) - \left(-3 \cos \tfrac{\pi}{2} - 2 \times \tfrac{\pi}{2}\right)$$

$$= (-3 \times (-1) - 2\pi) - (-3 \times 0 - \pi)$$

$$= 3 - 2\pi + \pi$$

$$= 3 - \pi$$

Now try these without a calculator:

Answers:
$1 - \frac{1}{e^3}$, 2, 2, 1.5

$$\int_0^3 e^{-x} \, dx, \ \int_3^4 (2x - 6)^3 \, dx, \ \int_{-2}^{-1} \left(\frac{1}{x^2} - x\right) dx, \ \int_0^{\frac{\pi}{3}} 3 \sin x \, dx$$

Area between two curves: No problem here: simply integrate to find the area under the first curve, do the same for the second curve, then subtract to find the area between them. Except that we can make life easier for ourselves by subtracting the two functions and simplifying **before** integrating, and we then only have one integral to do. It is also probable that we will have to find where the two curves intersect, as in the following example:

Find the points of intersection of the curves $y = x^2 + 6$ and $y = 12 + 4x - x^2$ and hence find the area enclosed between them.

The curves intersect when $x^2 + 6 = 12 + 4x - x^2$

$\therefore 2x^2 - 4x - 6 = 0 \Rightarrow x^2 - 2x - 3 = 0$

$(x - 3)(x + 1) = 0 \Rightarrow x = 3$ and $x = -1$

Points of intersection are $(3, 15)$ and $(-1, 7)$.

$$\text{Area enclosed} = \int_{-1}^{3} (12 + 4x - x^2) - (x^2 + 6) \, dx$$

$$= \int_{-1}^{3} -2x^2 + 4x + 6 \, dx$$

$$= \left[-\frac{2x^3}{3} + 2x^2 + 6x \right]_{-1}^{3}$$

$$= (-18 + 18 + 18) - \left(\frac{2}{3} + 2 - 6 \right)$$

$$= 21\tfrac{1}{3}$$

Here's a sketch of the two curves – but you don't need this to answer the question.

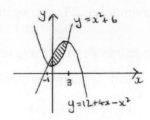

If we had subtracted the equations the other way around we would have ended up with a negative answer. But the area would still be positive.

If one of the curves is actually a straight line, it may be easier to use a standard area formula. On this graph, the area between the two curves is shaded green – we could find it by calculating the area under the curve, then subtracting the area of the blue triangle.

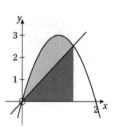

Kinematics problems: We first looked at kinematics problems in the differentiation section on page 95. Now we can cope with a full range of likely questions by using integration as well.

When position, velocity and acceleration are defined as functions of time, we can move from one to the other using the fact that velocity is rate of change of position, and acceleration is rate of change of velocity.

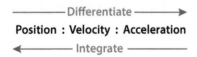

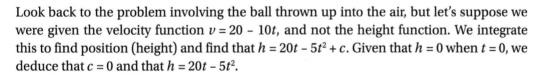

Look back to the problem involving the ball thrown up into the air, but let's suppose we were given the velocity function $v = 20 - 10t$, and not the height function. We integrate this to find position (height) and find that $h = 20t - 5t^2 + c$. Given that $h = 0$ when $t = 0$, we deduce that $c = 0$ and that $h = 20t - 5t^2$.

If we use a *definite* integral on v we will find the change in position over the given time interval, but we do need to be careful if there is a change of direction, as in fact there is at $t = 2$. This is why:

Change in position $t = 0$ to $t = 2$ is:

$$\int_{0}^{2} 20 - 10t \, dt = [20t - 5t^2]_{0}^{2} = 20 - 0 = 20$$

Change in position $t = 2$ to $t = 3$ is:

$$\int_{2}^{3} 20 - 10t \, dt = [20t - 5t^2]_{2}^{3} = 15 - 20 = -5$$

The negative change in position indicates we have reversed direction. So the integral from $t = 0$ to $t = 3$ will be $20 - 5 = 15$ which is its change in position compared to the start of the motion. If we want to know the total distance travelled we need to do the two separate integrals, then add the 20 upwards to the 5 downwards to get 25 m overall.

A neat way of doing this in one go using the GDC is to make use of the "absolute value" function. See if you can set this up on your GDC:

$$\int_0^3 |20 - 10t| \, dt$$

You should get 25, any negatives having been turned into positives.

Integration: Practice Exercise

1. Find the following indefinite integrals:

   (a) $\int 3x^2 + 5 - \frac{4}{x}\,dx$

   (b) $\int (1 - 2x)^3\,dx$

   (c) $\int \frac{1 + e^x}{e^x}\,dx$ *(Hint: Split into two fractions first)*

   (d) $\int \frac{2}{4x + 1}\,dx$

2. The diagram shows part of the curve of $y = 12x^2(1 - x)$. Find the x-intercepts, and hence write down an integral which represents the area enclosed by the curve and the x-axis. Evaluate the integral.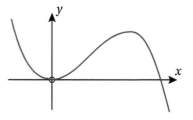

3. Let $f'(x) = 1 - x^2$. Given that $f(3) = 0$, find $f(x)$.

4. Given that $\int_0^{\frac{\pi}{2}} a - b \sin x\,dx = \frac{3\pi}{2} - 2$, find the values of a and b.

5. The acceleration of a particle at time t seconds is given by $a = 2t + \cos t$. Find:

   (a) The acceleration of the particle at $t = 1$.

   (b) The velocity, v, at time t, given that the initial velocity of the particle is 2 ms^{-1}

   (c) Find $\int_0^3 v\,dt$ What information does this give about the motion of the particle?

Calculus: Long Answer Questions

The answers to these section B style questions are given; full working can be found on the website.

1. Let $f(x) = \frac{4}{x} + 1$. Line L is the normal to the graph of f at the point where $x = 2$.

   (a) Show that the equation of L is $y = x + 1$.

   (b) Point A is the x-intercept of L. Find the coordinates of A.

   In the diagram below, the shaded region R is bounded by the x-axis, the graph of f, the line L and the line $x = 4$.

   (c) Find an expression for the area of R involving an integral.

   (d) Show that the area of R is $4\ln 2 + 6.5$

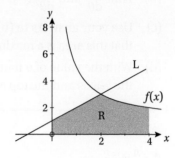

Answers:

(b) $(-1, 0)$

(c) Area $= \int_2^4 \frac{4}{x} + 1\ dx + 4.5$

2. Let $f(x) = \frac{2x}{x^2 + 4}$ where $x > 0$.

   (a) Show that $f'(x) = \frac{8 - 2x^2}{(x^2 + 4)^2}$

   (b) The graph of f has a maximum point. Find its coordinates.

   (c) Find $\int \frac{2x}{x^2 + 4}\ dx$

   (d) The area enclosed by the x-axis, the graph of f, and the lines $x = 1$ and $x = a$ is $\ln \frac{13}{5}$. Find the value of a.

Answers:

(b) $(2, 0.5)$ *Note the domain of f*

(c) $\ln(x^2 + 4) + c$

(d) $a = 3$

3. The diagram shows the graph of $f(x) = \cos\theta$ for $0 \leq \theta \leq \frac{\pi}{2}$.

   The rectangle A has opposite vertices at the origin and at a point on the graph with x-coordinate θ.

   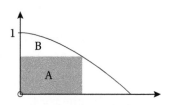

   (a) Write down the area, A, of the rectangle in terms of θ.

   (b) Find $\frac{dA}{d\theta}$ and $\frac{d^2A}{d\theta^2}$.

   (c) Use your answers to (b) to find the value of θ which makes A a maximum, and to justify that this area is a maximum.

   (d) With the value of θ found in (c), find area A and also the area of B enclosed by the curve, the y-axis and the top edge of A.

   _____

   Answers:

   (a) $A = \theta \cos\theta$

   (b) $\frac{dA}{d\theta} = -\theta\sin\theta + \cos\theta$; $\frac{d^2A}{d\theta^2} = -\theta\cos\theta - 2\sin\theta$

   (c) $\theta = 0.860$; Second derivative $= -2.08 < 0$

   (d) $A = 0.561$; $B = 0.197$

4. The function f has its derivative defined by $f'(x) = 3x^2 - px - 12$, where p is a constant.

   (a) Find $f''(x)$.

   (b) Given that the graph of f has a point of inflexion when $x = 1$, show that $p = 6$.

   (c) Find $f'(-2)$.

   The point P(-2, 3) lies on the graph of f.

   (d) Find the equation of the tangent to the curve of f at P, giving your answer in the form $ax + by = c$.

   (e) Find $f(x)$.

   _____

   Answers:

   (a) $f''(x) = 6x - p$

   (b) $6 \times 1 - p = 0 \Rightarrow p = 6$

   (c) $f'(-2) = 12$

   (d) $y - 12x = 27$

   (e) $f(x) = x^3 - 3x^2 - 12x - 1$

Chapter 6: MAXIMISING YOUR MARKS

Remember that the examiner is on your side – they want to give you marks! Make it easy for them to follow your thinking, even if you are not quite sure what you are doing or if you are getting wrong answers. You cannot lose marks for doing things wrong. LEARN THIS CHECKLIST.

Before you start a question:

- Read it carefully so you know what it is about.
- Highlight important words.

Answering a question:

- Check any calculations you do, preferably using a different method or order of operation.
- Show your working – there are often marks for method as well as for the right answer. And, in a longer question, a wrong answer at the start may mean lots more wrong answers – but the examiner will probably give you marks for correct methods, and will check your working against your original answer.
- Make sure you have answered *exactly* what the question asked. For example, have you been asked to calculate the new value of an investment or the amount of interest earned.
- In longer questions, don't worry if you can't work out the answer to a part. Carry on with the rest, using their answer (if one is given) or even making up a reasonable answer.

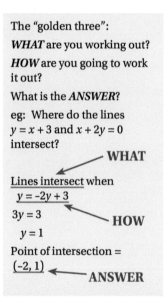

The "golden three":

WHAT are you working out?

HOW are you going to work it out?

What is the *ANSWER*?

eg: Where do the lines $y = x + 3$ and $x + 2y = 0$ intersect?

WHAT

Lines intersect when
$y = -2y + 3$
$3y = 3$
$y = 1$

HOW

Point of intersection = (–2, 1)

ANSWER

- Don't spend too long on any question or part of a question – you may lose the opportunity to answer easier questions later on. You can always come back and fill in gaps. Work to one mark per minute!
- Use words to explain what you are doing, especially in a longer question.
- The algebra can be tough – keep going!
- Check the units in questions – are they mixed?

Diagrams:

- Do not assume facts from diagrams, especially if they are marked NOT TO SCALE. For example, it may *look* like a right angle but does the question *tell* you that it is? Two lines may *look* parallel but they aren't unless you are *told* they are.
- And do draw your own diagrams - not necessarily to hand in as part of the question, but to help you sort out what's going on.

Key words in questions ("command terms"):

STATE: put the answer down without working (should be an easy one)!

WRITE DOWN: minimal working required.

> SHOW $x = 3$ is the solution of $2x + 1 = 7$.
>
> $2 \times 3 + 1 = 7$
>
> (We have not had to *solve* the equation)

SHOW: show enough working to get to the given answer.

EVALUATE: give a value to, work out.

SKETCH A GRAPH: draw its shape and show key points (eg: where it cuts the axes)

PLOT A GRAPH: work out points and draw the graph accurately

EXACT VALUE: not a rounded decimal eg: 2π, not 6.28...

When you have answered the question:

- Check you have answered every part of the question.
- Check you have answered exactly what was asked.
- Check you have answered to the correct accuracy (normally 3SF)
- Check that what you have written is clear, and that your answer is not mixed up in the working somewhere.

DO THESE CHECKS – you will probably pick up a few marks.

Chapter 7: PRACTICE QUESTIONS

The questions which follow are not designed to cover every aspect of the syllabus, nor are they exam style questions. Their purpose is to give you some practice in the *basics*: if you cannot, for example, carry out a straightforward differentiation, then you will get questions which depend on accurate differentiation wrong, even if you know exactly how to do the question. So you need to answer all these questions as part of your revision. If you get an answer wrong, find out why: then come back to it later, and see if you can get it right next time.

NUMBER AND ALGEBRA

1. Find the 25th term and the sum of the first 54 terms of the sequence which begins: 3, 8, 13, 18...

2. An arithmetic sequence has first term 7 and common difference 3.5. How many terms are required for the sum of the sequence to be 25830?

3. What is the 12th term and the sum to 18 terms of the sequence which begins 3, 12, 48, 192?

4. A geometric series has a first term 400, ten terms and a sum of 1295.67. What is the common ratio?

5. Find, without a calculator, the sum to infinity of the geometric series $-12 + 8 - \frac{16}{3}$.

6. Why does the sum to infinity exist for the sequence 100, 80, 64, 51.2? Find S_{20} and S_∞ and also the percentage error in approximating S_∞ by S_{20}.

7. How much will an investment of $6300 be worth (to the nearest dollar) after accumulating compound interest for 12 years at a rate of 3% per annum? If 1.5% interest is paid every 6 months, how much will the investment be worth after 12 years?

8. Write the following in standard form: 14500, 0.00303, 180 ÷ 1.5

9. Write $2 + 3\log_{10}x$ as a single logarithm.

10. Solve the equation $2\log_a x - \log_a 3 = \log_a 27$.

11. Solve the equation $\log_4 x - \log_4 7 = \frac{3}{2}$

12. Write as single powers of x: $\frac{1}{x^2}$, $(\sqrt{x})^5$, $(x^3)^4$, $x^2 \div x^{-5}$.

13. If $s = 3 + 10e^{0.4t}$, find t in the form $a \ln b$ when $s = 15$.

14. Use your GDC to solve $x + \log_3 x = 10$.

15. Find the constant term in the expansion of $\left(3x - \frac{1}{x}\right)^6$.

16. Without a calculator, work out the values of $^8C_2$, $^{10}C_1$, $^6C_3$, $^{12}C_2$

17. Find the value of (a) $\sum_1^{10}(3n-2)$, (b) $\sum_{11}^{20}(3n-2)$

FUNCTIONS

1. Find the range of the function $f(x) = \frac{x^3 - 2}{x}$, $x < 0$.

2. Find the largest possible domain of the function $f(x) = \frac{1}{\sqrt{9 - 4x^2}}$

3. Why is the inverse of $f(x) = x(x-2)$ not a function? Suggest a domain restriction which would ensure that $f^{-1}(x)$ *is* a function.

4. If $f(x) = x + 1$ and $g(x) = x^3$ find the function $(f \circ g)^{-1}$.

5. If $f(x) = 2x + 1$ and $g(x) = \cos x$ where $0 \le x \le \pi$, solve the equation $(g \circ f)(x) = 0.8$.

6. For the graph of $f(x) = \frac{e^{-x}}{(x+1)^2}$, identify any horizontal and vertical asymptotes. Find the turning point, and the solutions of the equation $f(x) = 7$.

7. What transformations for $y = x^2$ can be used to obtain the graph of $y = 2(x-3)^2 + 1$? Hence write down the turning point of the graph.

8. By considering transformations of $y = e^x$, sketch the graph of $y = -e^{(x+1)} + 2$. Mark the position to which the point $(0, 1)$ has been transformed.

9. Use the quadratic formula to solve $x + 3 = \frac{2}{x}$.

10. Complete the square for: $x^2 - 4x + 2$, $2x^2 + 6x + 5$, $12 - 2x - x^2$.

11. For each of the quadratics in 10, write down the turning point and the line of symmetry.

12. Find the range of values of k for which $2x^2 + 2x + k = 0$ has two real, distinct solutions.

13. Solve $3.1^x = 10^{x-1}$ giving your answer to 4DP.

14. Solve $e^{2x} - 7e^x + 6 = 0$ using quadratic factorisation. Give exact answers.

15. The graph with equation $y = 3^{2x} + k$ passes through the point $(1, 6)$. Find the value of k and find x when $y = -2$.

16. Sketch the graph of $y = \frac{x^2 + 1}{x - 3}$, and check your answer with a calculator.

17. State the axis intercepts and asymptotes of the graph of $y = \frac{2x - 1}{x + 2}$.

GEOMETRY AND TRIGONOMETRY

1. Convert to radians, giving answers in an exact form: 30°, 45°, 120°, 330°.

2. The sector of a circle with radius 5 cm has an arc length of 12 cm. Find the angle of the sector in radians, and its area.

3. Solve the equation $\cos 2\theta = \frac{1}{3}$, $0° \le \theta \le 360°$.

4. If $\sin \theta = \frac{3}{8}$ and θ is obtuse, find the exact values of $\cos \theta$ and $\tan \theta$.

5. Write down the equation of the function shown in the diagram in the form $y = a \sin(b(x + c))° + d$

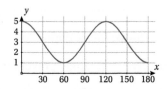

6. What is the range of the function $f(x) = 2\cos x°$ for $0° \le x \le 90°$?

For questions 7–10, use the trigonometric identities.

7. Solve $2\sin x = 5\cos x$, $0 \le x \le 2\pi$

8. Solve $2\sin x = \cos 2x$, $-180° \le x \le 180°$

9. Solve $2\sin 2\theta = 3\sin \theta$, $0 \le \theta \le \pi$

10. Solve $3\sin x = \tan x$, $0 \leq x \leq 360°$

11. Solve the following triangles (the triangle in each case is ABC):

    BC = 6 cm, C = 87°, A = 45°. Find AB.

    AB = 6 cm, A = 87°, AC = 5.4 cm. Find BC.

    AB = 6 cm, BC = 5.4 cm, CA = 3.5 cm. Find B.

    AB = BC = 5.2 cm. B = 34°. Find AC.

    AC = 6 cm, C = 32°, A = 90°. Find AB.

    BC = 6 cm, AB = 4 cm, C = 25°. Find A. (Two possibilities).

12. Find the area of the first and second triangles in question 11.

13. The sides of a triangle are x, $x + 1$ and p, where $p > x + 1$. If the largest angle is 120°, find an expression for p in terms of x. Find x if $p = \sqrt{7}$.

14. Write down exact values for $\sin\frac{\pi}{6}$, $\tan 45°$, $\cos\frac{3\pi}{2}$, $\sin 240°$, $\tan\frac{7\pi}{6}$, $\cos 315°$

15. A cylindrical tin has a closed base but is open at the top. Find its surface area and volume if $r = 3.5$ and $h = 6$.

16. A mast OT has is stabilised by two guy ropes, TA and TB, with angles of depression 65° and 20° respectively. OAB is a straight line. Given that the mast is 15 m tall, find the length AB, and the total length of rope required.

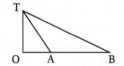

17. A square base pyramid has its apex directly above the centre of the base. If the base edge is 6 cm and the height of the pyramid is 9 cm, find the length of a slant edge, and the angle a slant edge makes with the base.

STATISTICS AND PROBABILITY

The amount spent (in €) by the first 50 people going into a shop is shown in the table below:

15.60	5.95	31.22	3.02	6.60	24.70	15.45	32.50	12.45	4.43
12.65	10.09	52.86	12.88	2.53	31.79	9.86	25.79	18.28	32.05
14.87	24.65	15.70	8.65	4.42	17.20	8.53	0.45	0.95	4.44
7.45	5.82	45.20	2.70	10.04	15.70	32.20	12.43	36.75	32.50
16.87	3.78	0.56	33.67	9.67	25.50	33.06	7.56	2.63	45.80

Questions 1 to 9 refer to this table.

1. Is this data discrete or continuous?

2. Draw up a grouped frequency table (with first group €0.01 – €10.00). You should have 6 groups.

3. Which is the modal group?

4. Enter the mid-values of each group and the frequencies onto your GDC. Calculate estimates of the mean and the standard deviation. (Why "estimates"?)

5. Draw a bar chart to represent the data.

6. Complete a cumulative frequency table for the data, and hence draw a cumulative frequency graph.

7. From the cumulative frequency graph, write down the median, the lower quartile, the upper quartile and calculate the interquartile range.

8. Draw a box and whisker plot for the data. Is the maximum value an outlier?

9. What was the least amount that the people in the top ten percentiles spent?

10. The mean of the numbers 1, 7, 8, 10, 11 and $k - 2$ is k. What extra number must be added to increase the mean to $k + 1$?

11. Use the data in the following table to calculate the correlation coefficient and the equation of the regression line of y on x.

x	1	4	4	6	8	10	11	12
y	30	28	36	30	39	35	40	44

12. Two dice are thrown. What is P(at least one shows a number greater than 1)?

13. I have 6 red socks and 4 green socks in a drawer. I take 2 out at random. Draw a tree diagram to show the possible outcomes and find P(the two socks do not match).

14. A and B are two events. P(A) = 0.2, P(B) = 0.5 and P(A ∪ B) = 0.55. Use a Venn diagram to find: P(A ∩ B); P(A' ∩ B); P(A|B); P(B'|A).

15. Given that $P(A) = \frac{2}{3}$, $P(B|A) = \frac{2}{5}$ and $P(B|A') = \frac{1}{4}$, find P(B') and P(A' ∪ B') without using a calculator.

16. Two dice are rolled. Find the probability that they show different numbers given that the total is 8.

17. Given that P(A ∪ B) = 0.7, P(A) = 0.6 and that A and B are independent events, find P(B).

18. The probability distribution for a discrete random variable X is as follows:

x	1	2	3	4	5
$P(X = x)$	0.3	0.35	k	$2k$	0.05

Find the value of k and the expected mean.

19. For $X \sim B(12, 0.2)$, find $P(X = 3)$, $P(X \leq 2)$, $P(X > 4)$. What is the mean of X?

20. For $X \sim B(6, p)$, $P(X = 5) = 0.393216$. Find p.

21. If $X \sim N(100, 5^2)$, find $P(X < 112)$, $P(X < 91)$, $P(95 < X < 101)$.

22. X is a normally distributed variable with $\mu = 18$. If $P(X > 20) = 0.115536$, find the standard deviation.

CALCULUS

1. Differentiate $(2x - 1)^3$ using the chain rule. Expand $(2x - 1)^3$ and show that differentiating the expanded function gives the same result.

2. Differentiate these functions: (a) xe^{-x} (b) $\cos^2 2x$ (c) $4\sqrt{x} - 5$ (d) $2\ln(\cos x)$ (e) $\frac{x^2 - 2}{x}$ (f) $\frac{3x^3}{(x + 1)}$ (g) $\sqrt{x^3 - 2}$ (h) $\frac{x^2}{\tan x}$ (i) $\ln(3 - x^2)$

3. Given that $f(x) = x(x^2 - 3)$ find the coordinates of any stationary points and hence the values of x for which f is an increasing function.

4. Find the equations of the tangent and normal to $y = 3\ln x$ at the point with x-coordinate 3.

5. Find the first and second derivatives of $y = xe^x$.

6. For the graph of the function $f(x) = \frac{x - 1}{x}$ find: any axis intercepts; the vertical asymptote; the behaviour for large $|x|$; any turning points. Hence sketch the graph.

7. Find the point of inflexion on the graph of $f(x) = x^3 - 3x^2 + 1$. What is the gradient at the point of inflexion?

8. The perimeter of a rectangle is a cm. If its width is x cm, find its length in terms of a and x. Prove that the area is a maximum when all sides are the same length.

9. Integrate these functions: (a) $\int \sin 3x \, dx$ (b) $\int x(2x-3) \, dx$ (c) $\int 2 \sin x \cos x \, dx$ (d) $\int \sqrt{2x-3} \, dx$ (e) $\int -e^{0.1x} \, dx$ (f) $\int \frac{1}{(2-x)^2} \, dx$

10. Find the real number $k > 1$ for which $\int_1^k \left(1 + \frac{1}{x^2}\right) dx = \frac{3}{2}$

11. Find the area enclosed by the curve $y = 4x - x^2$ and the x-axis.

12. Find the area enclosed between the curves $y = 2x^2 + 3$ and $y = 10x - x^2$.

13. Find $f(x)$ if $f'(x) = \frac{3}{x+1}$ and $y = 3$ when $x = 1$.

14. The displacement s of a particle from an origin O at time t seconds is $s = 2t^2 - 3t + 6$. Find the displacement, the velocity and the acceleration of the particle when $t = 1.5$.

15. A particle moves in a straight line. At time t secs its acceleration is given by $a = 3t - 1$. When $t = 0$, the velocity of the particle is $2\,\text{ms}^{-1}$ and it is $3\,\text{m}$ from the origin. Find expressions for v and s in terms of t. Show that the particle is always moving away from the origin.

16. If $y = e^{-x} \cos x$, determine the three values of x between 0 and 3π for which $\frac{dy}{dx} = 0$. Show that the corresponding values of y form a geometric progression with common ratio $-e^{-\pi}$.

Answers to Practice Questions

NUMBER AND ALGEBRA

1. 123, 7317
2. 120
3. 12 582 912, 6.87×10^{10}
4. 0.7
5. -7.2
6. $r = 0.8$, 494.24, 500, 1.15%
7. $8982, $9006
8. 1.45×10^5, 3.03×10^{-3}; 1.2×10^2
9. $2.5 \ln 1.2$
10. 9
11. 56
12. $x^{-2}, x^{\frac{2}{3}}, x^{12}, x^7$
13. 1.8
14. 8.096
15. -540
16. 28, 10, 20, 66
17. 145, 445

FUNCTIONS

1. $f(x) \geq 3$
2. $-1.5 < x < 1.5$
3. More than 1 y-value for a given x-value; $x \geq 1$ (others possible)
4. $\sqrt[3]{(x-1)}$
5. 2.32 or 2.96
6. $y = 0$, $x = -1$, $(-3, 5.02)$, $x = -4.38$ or -0.512 or -2.06
7. Translation $\binom{3}{0}$, stretch $\times 2$ parallel to y-axis, translation $\binom{0}{1}$; (3, 1).
8.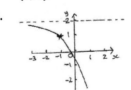
9. $\frac{-3 \pm \sqrt{17}}{2}$
10. $(x-2)^2 - 2$, $2(x+1.5)^2 + 0.5$, $13 - (x+1)^2$
11. $(2, -2)$, $x = 2$; $(-1.5, 0.5)$, $x = -1.5$; $(-1, 13)$, $x = -1$
12. $k < 0.5$
13. 1.9660
14. $0, \ln 6$
15. $-3, 0$
16. check with calculator
17. $(0, -0.5)$, $(0.5, 0)$, $x = -2$, $y = 2$

GEOMETRY AND TRIGONOMETRY

1. $\dfrac{\pi}{6}, \dfrac{\pi}{4}, \dfrac{2\pi}{3}, \dfrac{11\pi}{6}$

2. 2.4, 30

3. 54.7°, 125.3°, 234.7°, 305.3°

4. $-\dfrac{\sqrt{55}}{8}, -\dfrac{3}{\sqrt{55}}$

5. $y = 2\sin(3(x + 30)) + 3$

6. $0 \le f(x) \le 2$

7. 1.19, 4.33

8. 21.5°, 158.5°

9. $0, \pi, 0.723$

10. 0°, 70.5°, 180°, 289.5°, 360°

11. 8.47, 7.86, 35.3°, 3.04, 3.75, 39.3° or 140.7°

12. 18.9, 16.2

13. $p = \sqrt{3x^2 + 3x + 1}, x = 1$

14. $\dfrac{1}{2}, 1, 0, -\dfrac{\sqrt{3}}{2}, \dfrac{1}{\sqrt{3}}, \dfrac{\sqrt{2}}{2}$

15. 170.4, 230.9

16. 34.2 m, 60.4 m

17. 9.95 cm, 64.8°

STATISTICS AND PROBABILITY

1. Discrete.

2.
0.01 – 10.00	10.01 – 20.00	20.01 – 30.00	30.01 – 40.00	40.01 – 50.00	50.01 – 60.00
20	14	5	8	2	1

3. 0.01 – 10.00

4. 17.2, 13.31; not using original data.

5.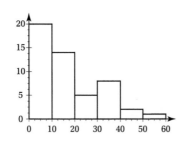

6.
€	≤10	≤20	≤30	≤40	≤50	≤60
c.f.	20	34	39	47	49	50

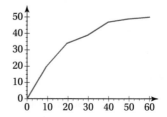

7. $Q_1 = 6, Q_2 = 14, Q_3 = 28$, IQR = 22

   No. $Q_3 + 1.5 \times$ IQR = 61

8.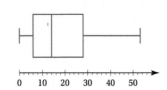

9. €38

10. 14

11. 0.796, $y = 1.15x + 27.2$

12. 35/36

13. P(no match) = 8/15; see diagram:

14. 0.15, 0.35, 0.3, 0.25

15. $\dfrac{13}{20}, \dfrac{11}{15}$

16. 0.8

17. 0.25

18. 0.1, 2.35.

19. 0.236, 0.558, 0.0726; 2.4

20. 0.8

21. 0.992, 0.0359, 0.421

22. 1.67

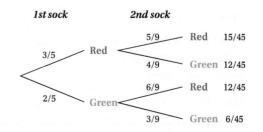

CALCULUS

1. $6(2x-1)^2$

2. (a) $e^{-x}(1-x)$, (b) $-4\sin 2x \cos 2x$, (c) $\dfrac{2}{\sqrt{x}}$,
   (d) $-2\tan x$, (e) $1+\dfrac{2}{x^2}$, (f) $\dfrac{3x^2(2x+3)}{(x+1)^2}$,
   (g) $\dfrac{3x^2}{2\sqrt{x^3-2}}$, (h) $\dfrac{2x\sin x \cos x - x^2}{\sin^2 x}$,
   (i) $-\dfrac{2x}{3-x^2}$

3. $(-1,2)$, $(1,-2)$; $x<-1$ or $x>1$

4. $y=x-3+3\ln 3$, $y=-x+3-3\ln 3$

5. $e^x(x+1)$, $e^x(x+2)$

6. $(1,0)$; $x=0$; $f(x)\to 1$; None.

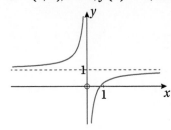

7. $(1,-1)$, -3

8. $\frac{1}{2}a-x$

9. (a) $-\frac{1}{3}\cos 3x + c$, (b) $\frac{2}{3}x^3 - \frac{3}{2}x^2 + c$,
   (c) $-\frac{1}{2}\cos 2x + c$ or $-\cos^2 x + c$ or $\sin^2 x + c$, (d) $\frac{1}{3}(2x-3)^{\frac{3}{2}}+c$,
   (e) $-10e^{0.1x}+c$, (f) $\frac{1}{2-x}+c$

10. 2

11. $10\frac{2}{3}$

12. 9.48

13. $y=3\ln(x+1)+3+\ln 2$

14. $6, 3, 4$

15. $v=1.5t^2-t+2$, $s=0.5t^3-0.5t^2+2t+3$

    $v\neq 0$ for any value of t (discriminant <0). So v is always positive, and particle is moving away from the origin.

16. $\frac{3}{4}\pi, \frac{7}{4}\pi, \frac{11}{4}\pi$